W9-CAV-288

Front cover: Norman Sperling
Back cover: Dennis di Cicco

THE CLOUDY NIGHT BOOK

AN ASTRONOMER'S COMPANION:

A Collection of Puzzles, Word Games, and
Miscellanea To While Away Tedious Moments
Until the Sky Finally Clears

by

GEORGE S. MUMFORD

SKY PUBLISHING CORPORATION
Cambridge, Massachusetts

THE CLOUDY NIGHT BOOK

© Sky Publishing Corporation 1979

All rights reserved. Except for brief passages quoted in a review, no part of this book may be reproduced by any mechani-
cal, photographic, or electronic process, nor may it be stored in
an information retrieval system, transmitted, or otherwise
copied for public or private use, without the written permission
of the publisher.

The signs and symbols reproduced on pages 4, 6, 20, 23, 29,
31, 35, 38, 43, 47, 48, 53, 64, 70, 88, 94, 95, 100, 106, 108,
111, 112, 113, 114, and 115 are from *Symbols, Signs & Signets*
by Ernst Lehner, published by Dover Publications, Inc., 1950.

First printing, 1979

Library of Congress catalog card number 78-63246

ISBN   0-933346-00-X

Dedication

To all observers who have lost their place
in history because the night was cloudy.

Preface

Especially when I have telescope time, but on most other occasions too, I am an impulsive sky watcher. On a night when the clouds come and go, I can't concentrate for long on any one project. No problem when the rain is pouring down; but when I have to run out of the dome every few minutes to see what the status of the sky is, that's another matter. Puzzles, word games, and the like, provide food for thought over brief interludes, so whenever I head for a mountaintop, a book of crossword puzzles goes along.

Then it occurred to me that maybe another way to pass some time would be to combine my word-game interest with astronomy, both for entertainment and perhaps for education. From that thought, the present volume arose.

Stories of what happens on cloudy nights at an observatory are legion. I have not even dented the surface with the lore included here. Golf cart races at Cerro Tololo, Pisco parties — I've heard about them. I've also heard that the ghost of James Lick frequently prevents an astronomer from leaving the observing floor of the 36-inch refractor before the sky has completely clouded over. Send along your contributions — lore, puzzles, problems, and astronomical oddities. I'll compile them for a future edition and will eventually send you a reply.

G. S. M., 1979
P. O. Box 267
Dover, MA 02030

Contents

Cloudy Night Lore

HOW MANY ASTRONOMERS, I wonder, are not immortalized with a textbook reference because the night was cloudy. Are there comets out there, for example, bearing the name Seki that might otherwise have been known as Comet Adams or Comet Bernstein?

There are some historical precedents. I recall reading somewhere, and it's probably true, that on January 6, 1610, the German astronomer Simon Marius planned to observe Jupiter through a recently acquired telescope. However, the night was cloudy. Hence, it was left for Galileo Galilei to discover the four bright moons of Jupiter during the following nights.

But the discovery of Io, Europa, Ganymede, and Callisto, names given by Marius, called for persistence — a continuing series of observations over a period of time. History tells us that Marius likely had observed these satellites during the autumn of 1609, but he did not truly appreciate the remarkable thing he had stumbled upon. One can hardly blame cloudy nights.

Other examples exist to indicate that factors aside from cloudy nights can deny persons their place in history. Take, for instance, Professor J. Challis of Cambridge University and the search for Neptune. When, belatedly, he took up the search using John Couch Adams' predicted position, he had to make a night-by-night plot of the area of the sky he viewed. These charts piled up, and Challis didn't take the time to compare them. If he had, he would have found the position of one object to have changed. Thus, he would have recognized Neptune some time ahead of Johann Gottfried Galle.

Between 1914 and 1916, Percival Lowell and E. O. Lampland began photographing a strip along the ecliptic where it was anticipated the trans-Neptunian planet would be located. The lens they used had been borrowed from Swarthmore College's Sproul Observatory. Some years later, following Clyde Tombaugh's discovery of Pluto, these old photographic plates were looked at again. On several a very faint image of the planet appeared. Apparently, it had been overlooked by Lowell and Lampland who were searching for something they believed to be brighter.

A number of years ago during the autumn, I was assigned a couple of nights on the 24-inch reflector at Harvard's Agassiz Station. I had just become interested in the question of whether one might be able to detect eclipsing binaries among the novalike variables. Though these stars are generally quite faint at minimum light, when they are best observed to uncover such details, I felt that I should be able to study U Geminorum. This star is, of course, the prototype of the so-called dwarf novae, and it flares up in brightness some four or more magnitudes every 80 to 100 days. In any event, I was all set to undertake the photoelectric observations, only to be wiped out by a cloudy night. About a week later the Polish astronomer, later a collaborator, Voytek Krzeminski showed that U Geminorum was indeed an eclipsing binary. I had lost my spot in history due to a cloudy night. Not so, it later turned out. U Geminorum was below the detection level of Harvard's 24-inch reflector.

Thus, when you miss the observations that were going to lead to a remarkable discovery, maybe it was because the night was cloudy, but experience shows there are other factors too!

More Cloudy Night Lore

AT MIDNIGHT it was raining hard on the mountain when a fellow astronomer decided to change from the 9:00 a.m. flight east to the red-eye special that left some five hours earlier.

By 1:30 that morning he had reached the terminal, turned in the rented car, and had downed a double scotch in preparation for a solid sleep on the long flight ahead. He was astonished by the number of travelers congregating at Gate 5. And after the plane arrived from San Diego, there was considerable delay in loading as the airline personnel sought to find everyone a seat. Being among the last to board, he was bumped up to first class since the tourist section had already been filled.

Given that he had worked hard the previous five nights and was returning with a wealth of data, he felt he deserved first-class treatment, a good meal, and free drinks. At 15,000 feet, the plane passed through the cloud layer, and out of the porthole he could see Antares. At 30,000 feet, the plane leveled off. Drinks, dinner, a pillow; shortly he was sound asleep.

But then he awoke with a start; it seemed as though the plane had turned. He looked through the porthole; now the Big Dipper was in view. At that moment the voice of the captain rasped from the loudspeakers announcing that the plane was returning to Tucson as a warning had just been received that a bomb might be on board.

The plane touched down about 4:30 and rolled to a stop some distance from the terminal. Passengers and crew crowded off and stood for some time waiting at the edge of the runway for instructions or something to happen. Eventually all moved back to Gate 5, which they had left some hours earlier, to be met by hoots and shouts from three passengers who had been bumped from the flight.

At 2:00 a.m. the Tucson terminal is dull; at 6:00 a.m. it is deadly. The astronomer strolled around, waiting word on what was going to happen and watching for sunrise — still cloudy. Minutes ticked by. At 7:30 it was possible to buy a newspaper. At 8:00 he watched the lucky trio that had been bumped take off for Chicago and elsewhere. He should have been in Chicago by now. Back to waiting.

Finally, the announcement: the flight was ready to reboard. The plane had been searched and one passenger and his luggage removed — ha! ha! As passengers lined up to pass through the metal detector, he hurriedly called East to alert those awaiting him as to his whereabouts. Leaving the phone, he ducked under the metal rail that split the concourse to divide the flow of traffic. Then it happened. He heard a loud pop, and gingerly felt his seat. Yes, he had split the seam of his pants.

He backed under the rail and up to the wall. His overcoat was safely ensconced on the plane in his bag. There he stood, trying to decide what to do next. A janitor was sweeping the floor a short way down the concourse. He sidled along the wall in his direction. "Have you got any safety pins?" he asked. "No" was the response.

Leaning against the wall, he saw three stewardesses chatting a short way off. "Aha!" he thought. As an all-night listener to "Music Till Dawn," sponsored by American Airlines, he knew that those gals are supposed to be prepared for all emergencies. He sidled up to the group and asked if by chance any of them had a needle and thread handy.

"What for?"

"To fix my pants, I ripped the seam."

"Turn around. You certainly did!"

"What about a safety pin?"

"No," said one of the stewardesses, . . . "but wait, have you got a dime?"

He searched his pockets and produced one. She disappeared into the ladies room and returned with a small package containing two safety pins and a product commonly used by women. He ducked into the men's room to effect the necessary repairs.

Now he was at the end of the line in front of the metal detector. When his turn came, he passed through and was halted by a sharp squeal; metal was present. He took off his jacket, removed all keys and coins from his pockets, and tried again. Once more the loud squeal, which now alerted a number of passengers and hangers-on to a potentially interesting situation. He tried a third time. Again the squeal. With that he bent over. "It must be the safety pins," he pointed out to the attendant.

Funny thing though, he had no trouble in Chicago.

Sun (Sunday)
*Gypsy Planet and
Dream Book*

— 4 —

And More . . .

HE NOTED, as he walked to the Tucson terminal in the afternoon sunlight, that cirrus was showing in the west. Well, maybe tonight wouldn't be good, but with five more .... . About an hour later, when he turned the rented car off the road to Sells and onto the mountain road, the cirrus had become higher and thicker. No, there would be no observing that night, nor as it turned out the next, or the next, or the next!

By the afternoon of the fifth day, with the clouds still hanging over the mountain, the astronomer was becoming stir crazy. There was nothing of interest left to read among the small collection of books that constituted the Mountain Branch of the Tucson Public Library; games of pool, both solitary and with night assistants, had lost their appeal; he was up-to-date on the various reports and other materials he had brought to read, review, and write. No, he just couldn't face another long, dull, cloudy night on the mountain.

The weather forecast indicated no improvement for the next three days, and charts in the newspaper seemed to support this view. After considerable hesitation, our astronomer dialed some friends in Tucson and made arrangements to meet them for dinner — what a break to get away from the starchy diet on the mountain. Following the late-afternoon weather forecast, which, if anything, called for a further deterioration in conditions, he backed his car out of the parking lot and was soon headed down the mountain on the first leg of the 60-mile trip back to civilization. He paused briefly at the Sells road. The mountain was covered with clouds; no breaks were visible in any direction and there was not even an indication of a sunset glow. He stepped on the gas.

Dinner was long and leisurely, with good wine, good food, good conversation. Before dessert, he excused himself and took a peek outside. As his eyes became dark adapted, there was Sirius shining brilliantly in the sky. Yes, there were Orion and the Pleiades too! There was no trace of clouds, not even a wisp of fuzz around Jupiter. The astronomer rushed back inside, threw some bills on the table, and dashed to his car. He pulled out of the parking lot in a cloud of dust and shortly was on Ajo Way, and the road to Sells.

He paused briefly at Ryan Field, some 15 miles outside the Tucson city limits — yes, the sky *was* clear. Hurdling over dips, he was hitting close to 75 when he took the right turn at Three Points, the last hamlet before the mountain road, still some 20 miles away. On through the night he raced, thanking heaven that there were no cattle wandering across the road in this open range. Minutes ticked on and on. Finally, he saw the welcome warning of the intersection ahead and a mile later turned left to make the final dash to the summit still 12 miles up the mountain road. But there, ahead in the beam of the headlights, was a bar across the road. The gate was closed. He pulled up to it and got out. The key for the padlock was always in an opening at the top of the left post. But the cap on the post would not come off. In desperation he tried the caps on all the posts; none would budge. Then he noticed that the gate was on a bridge crossing a wash, and he suddenly realized that this was a new gate and that he had no idea where the key might be.

Back to the car, a quick U-turn, back to the road, back toward Tucson — he had to find a telephone. No lights at Three Points, the general store had long since closed. Likewise, the lunchroom at Ryan Field was dark. Finally, an hour after leaving the gate, he came upon a Circle K, open 24 hours. He pulled up with tires shrieking and dashed to the phone.

After what seemed an interminable period, it was answered. "It's Dr. X," he said, "where's the key to the gate?"

"Why, on a panel below the 'No Trespassing' sign to the right," said the night cook. "I thought everyone knew that." Dr. X didn't answer. Back to the car, past Ryan Field, Three Points, to the gate. By now more than three hours had elapsed. The key was there. Tires squealed as he hurtled around hairpin turns during the half hour drive to the top of the mountain. Thank heavens again, he thought; there had been no rock slides. Up, up — at last the final turn. Straight to his telescope he drove.

Up to the dome he raced; the slit was opened; and the photometer loaded with crushed dry ice. In half an hour he would be able to start observing. He caught his breath, and then fixed on a program star. He activated the photometer and started to watch the wiggles of the pen on the recorder chart. And then, the pen dropped to the bottom. Dr. X looked toward the slit; the sky had clouded over.

As a consequence of this experience, the gate to the mountain road to this day — or rather to this night — remains unlocked.

The Hour

And More . . .

I WAS INTRODUCED to the operation of a university observatory in the summer of 1946 when, through the intercession of my preparatory school mentor, Albert E. Navez, Bart Bok invited me to work at Harvard's Agassiz Station. I was delighted.

To this day, I still wonder how Navez met Bok or vice-versa. Albert was a school teacher. He had started his career as a surgeon with the Belgian army and then came to the United States. He taught biology and chemistry and seemed to have a real, though somewhat superficial interest in astromony. He was a member of the Bond Club and the American Association of Variable Star Observers; perhaps it was through a meeting at Harvard that he had met the university professor and professional astronomer with whom I have had a lifelong association.

My principal duties that summer were to run the patrol cameras and the 8-inch photographic telescope. As I recall, the June nights were short, pleasant, and relatively bug free. Things settled down pretty much to a routine after I had at least twice pulled the standard beginners trick of taking a carefully guided four-hour exposure only to find, upon development, that I had forgotten to open the telescope's shutter.

Early in July the haze began thickening, and a series of "Arcturus nights" commenced. We would open the telescopes, get everything prepared, and then climb to the catwalk adjacent to the patrol cameras. This was the best location for an overall view of the sky, unless you wanted to climb the fire lookout tower a half-mile away.

As the sky darkened, Bok would join the crew consisting of the Jesuit Father LeClaire, Joe Gossner, who was then a Harvard graduate student, Henry Sawyer, the first professional night assistant I ever ran across, and myself. Bok would sniff the heavy air, look over the sky, mutter something about not being able to see any star fainter than Arcturus, and then head off to his quarters in the "Summer Palace," which he shared with the Father.

For the rest of us, our entertainment on an Arcturus night was getting Henry to talk, not that this took any particular effort. A simple question such as "How's your car running, Henry?" and he would be off for two, three, or even four hours of absolute nonstop talking. I'd listen for a bit, then go away to check the sky. Upon returning, Henry would still be talking.

Harold Spencer Jones, the great British astronomer, once visited the Agassiz Station. Becoming tired of wandering around from dome to dome, he came into the administration building for a rest. "Great conversationalist, that man," reported Henry, "we chatted for three hours. Smart fellow." The truth of the matter, I later heard, was that Spencer Jones slept for three hours while Henry talked.

Favorite topics that I remember included marriage problems; construction of a cellar under an existing house; care and feeding of Henry's five cars with an average age of 15 years; how Robert Baker had stolen all his telescope designs; why Harlow Shapley should let Henry have complete control of the observing program. Henry would ensconce himself in an easy chair, light a foul-smelling stogey, open his mouth, and was off. I can see him now, wreathed in smoke, playing with a variety of lenses and talking, talking, talking.

Then, from time to time, would come one of those nights when it wasn't even worth opening up the domes. At Bok's invitation we would repair to the "Summer Palace" for beer and conversation — hence the obvious name, "Beer Nights." He would regale us with stories of astronomers he knew. One beer night that I remember in particular was during August, after the radio had just flashed word of a tremendous bomb blast on the Japanese city of Hiroshima. On that night Bok described what he knew of the Manhattan Project and the development of the atom bomb by his colleagues from Harvard and other institutions.

I didn't get the opportunity for much observing during my undergraduate years. As the war wound down graduate students returned, and they took most of the time available during the summer. It was hard to fit a night or two into the regular academic schedule. I do recall a couple of winter nights though, when the temperature became so low that I was unable to close the dome of the 61-inch telescope in the morning.

Though my thesis at Indiana University was supposedly on an observational topic, once again I didn't get in much time and don't recall anything special about cloudy nights. The reason for the lack of telescope time available to graduate students, I realized in later years, was that the assistant professors on the faculty were then readying themselves for tenure review. The "publish or perish" syndrome may be what led one of these faculty members to report, upon returning from a stay at McDonald Observatory, that the Texas sky was so good he was able to continue photoelectric observations between the cumulus clouds! You've got to get the observations, if you're going to publish. And you certainly have to publish in order to become a member of the faculty elite.

At the University of Virginia, the problem was purely and simply the combination of an antique refracting telescope and weather. Fragments of nights over a two-year span allowed me finally to piece together sufficient data.

One July night the telephone rang. All around were thunderheads; Mars was also prominent at that time, being quite close to opposition.

"Hello," I said.

"I've been watchin' a flyin' sausor and was wonderin' if yo'all had seen it," a feminine voice replied.

"No Ma'am, but I have seen Mars appear to duck in and out of the clouds."

"What yo'all mean Mars. That's a flyin' sausor, git out and look fo' yo'self."

So out I went, to see wisps of clouds passing across Mars and causing the planet truly to look as though it were moving in and out of them. Back to the phone.

"I looked, Ma'am, and it's still Mars."

The phone was recradled, and I went about other things. Somewhat over an hour later, with the sky still virtually unchanged, the phone rang again.

"Hello."

"Oh, you. Hav' yo'all seen that sausor yet?"

"No ma'am. Futhermore, it's not a saucer, it's Mars."

Back to my business. Time passed. Eventually the phone rang again.

"Hello."

"Oh. So yo'ah still there!" There was a click. No mo' calls came.

And More...

AT KITT PEAK several years ago, a number of us were sitting around after dinner having a second, third, or even fourth cup of coffee. It was a weekend. Except for a skeleton maintenance staff and those necessary to keep the rambunctious public under control, virtually everyone else was a professional or soon to be professional astronomer. The solar group was there too, joining those of us about to go on night duty. But, since the cirrus was yet quite thick, no one was in a hurry to move — conversation, coffee, and procrastination.

Then came a shriek from the general direction of the kitchen. A distraught cook reported that as she opened the door to take out the night's garbage, a skunk had run right into the kitchen. The alert girl Friday — general factotum — had quickly opened the door to a broom closet, and the skunk disappeared within. Thus, the problem facing some of the great (or would be) brains in astronomy that night was how to get a skunk out of a kitchen broom closet and into the healthy, invigorating night air.

Needless to say, debate waxed hot and heavy. There were those who took the position that an early death was the only way. Others spoke in terms of family ties, the possibility that this was the bread winner, the chief taxpayer, etc. The latter group won out.

A general plan was formulated. Obviously, the skunk had been attracted by the aroma arising from preparation of the evening meal. Maybe this could be used to entice it out of the closet and off the premises. Someone suggested laying a track of lettuce leaves. Seemed like a great idea. A trail of lettuce was laid from the broom closet, around the work table, and as directly as possible to the back door. Positions were assigned. The leader grabbed a broom and took a spot in the middle of the room, so as to urge the skunk along, he explained. Two others were assigned to either door.

The signal was given. Both doors, to the closet and to the outer world, were thrown open in a feat of timing reminiscent of a rocket launching. The skunk from the closet behaved as predicted; out he or she came along the path of lettuce. But simultaneously, another skunk came bolting in — not, however, with quite the rapidity that a number of the great brains in astronomy left!

Astrobits

NAME THAT TUNE ABOUT THE MOON

There are a good many titles of songs that involve the moon. Use the clues at the right to help you find each title. The word lengths are indicated by the lengths of the lines.

A. _____Moon	County or river
B. _____Moon	State
C. _____Moon	State minus North or South
D. _____Moon	River
E. _____Moon	Certainly not green cheese
F. _____Moon	Song of the astronauts?
G. _____Moon	Candy
H. __Moon____	Setting
I. __Moon	Crescent
J. _____Moon	Command to moon in autumn
K. Moon_____	Above a city
L. ____Moon	Tired?
M. __Moon_____	Cause of the accident
N. _____Moon	Rarely
O. _____Moon	Likely a good spot to avoid
P. _____Moon?	About 250,000 miles
Q. _____Moon	You dog you
R. ____Moon	Color in the spectrum
S. _____Moon	Color not in the spectrum
T. _____Moon_____	Kate Smith theme

Answers: page 96

CRYPTOGRAMS

A feature of a planet is described in each of the following statements. The actual length of the word is indicated by the number of letters that have been substituted for the correct ones. If you need a hint, the location of the planet's name in each sentence is given on page 89. In each case the code differs.

1. IXWFBIX SCU DIGV FYD MIDYI UCFXGGKFXU.

2. ZCIREM NZ MPI IQB PMSA GSCMBI XNIQ ENMOZ.

3. ABQFZQN LO DEB RIGSBD FIXOBOD DX DEB OZS.

4. LXORY FY WCXMRXODUQ JKUUXE DIX XKCDI'Y YFYDXC GUKOXD.

5. AFV XCEA XWEENBV LYWJVA NJ AFV ECYWD EMEAVX NE OKLNAVD.

6. KIB FXDPBEK JGFQXAG WAGZA UE AUC GFRTHUQX GA TXDE.

7. FQY AXBF DYAXFY CEZWYF CDYBYWFEG UWXJW MB CEKFX.

8. PBS ACPZPYCFZQ ZDYV CW XAZFXV QYSV ZQGCVP YF PBS SUQYJPYU.

Answers: page 96

— 12 —

SONGS FOR A CLOUDY NIGHT

The weather has socked in; it's time for a sing-along. Gather your cohorts and try these suggestions, but you'll have to untangle the titles.

1. WAILESSRPORH
2. RATHERWETMOSY
3. LLBNTIUAYMSFAEBHTRA
4. NNNNIIIIGSEARTH
5. YDGOAAYGF
6. NGIGEBITAGOWHOLNHSHSENONO?
7. 'SNAGGEIBLLTTEOOIMNNE
8. SENENENTTWTSTWTTWLLLSIOIOIO
9. TSIYM
10. YLOSULETLTBLRDOCHLI
11. NLSIOGOTFA
12. EEWNOURHOFTO
13. YSLMETBLOEUTRIKK
14. RIOTEOFORHNNA
15. EASIRHYDHMCNAETAET

Answers: page 96

WORDIES

I sometimes take a sheet of paper, write a word such as CONSTEL-LATION, and see how many four-letter or longer words I can make from its letters. Plurals do not count, even those of three-letter words. Further, I use only noun or verb forms, the noun or adjective form, but not both. The individual letters of the source word are used only once, and the derived word must be in a standard unabridged dictionary.

From C L U S T E R, you should be able to make more than 30 words.

1. _____	11. _____	21. _____
2. _____	12. _____	22. _____
3. _____	13. _____	23. _____
4. _____	14. _____	24. _____
5. _____	15. _____	25. _____
6. _____	16. _____	26. _____
7. _____	17. _____	27. _____
8. _____	18. _____	28. _____
9. _____	19. _____	29. _____
10. _____	20. _____	30. _____

Answers: page 97

Now that you have the method, try P L A N E T S. At least 69 words
are possible.

1. _____	24. _____	47. _____
2. _____	25. _____	48. _____
3. _____	26. _____	49. _____
4. _____	27. _____	50. _____
5. _____	28. _____	51. _____
6. _____	29. _____	52. _____
7. _____	30. _____	53. _____
8. _____	31. _____	54. _____
9. _____	32. _____	55. _____
10. _____	33. _____	56. _____
11. _____	34. _____	57. _____
12. _____	35. _____	58. _____
13. _____	36. _____	59. _____
14. _____	37. _____	60. _____
15. _____	38. _____	61. _____
16. _____	39. _____	62. _____
17. _____	40. _____	63. _____
18. _____	41. _____	64. _____
19. _____	42. _____	65. _____
20. _____	43. _____	66. _____
21. _____	44. _____	67. _____
22. _____	45. _____	68. _____
23. _____	46. _____	69. _____

Answers: page 97

Some words do not provide many possibilities. D E N E B, for
example, gives BEEN, BENE, DENE, BEND, and NEED. However, add
-OLA for D E N E B O L A and you should be able to construct some 50
additional words.

Answers: page 98

DIVIDING THE UNIVERSE

Have you ever wondered what would happen if you divided the sun into planets, or a quasar into the universe? Now you can find out. The object, of course, is to replace the letters by numbers that yield a valid result.

A.

```
            N P E T
SUN ) P L A N E T
      S U N
      ─────
      A A U N
      U T S P
      ─────
        A P S E
        A A F E
        ─────
          A E B T
          A P E T
          ─────
            U B
```

0 =	5 =
1 =	6 =
2 =	7 =
3 =	8 =
4 =	9 =

B.

```
                  R I R
QUASAR ) U N I V E R S E
         E V U E E S
         ─────────
         S R E A U S
         V S A M U N
         ─────────
           E U A M R E
           E V U E E S
           ─────────
             I M N E Q
```

0 =	5 =
1 =	6 =
2 =	7 =
3 =	8 =
4 =	9 =

C.

```
          A R M
GAS ) S P I R A L
      F G A
      ─────
      A A M A
      A S P R
      ─────
        S A L L
        S A I M
        ─────
          S G
```

0 =	5 =
1 =	6 =
2 =	7 =
3 =	8 =
4 =	9 =

```
                I E I E L
D.  MOON  ) S A T E L L I T E
            S S L T N
            E E N T L
             M O O N
             S S N T I
             S S L T N
               M P N T
               M O O N
                 I S S E
                 L L L L
                 I S S E
```

0 =   5 =
1 =   6 =
2 =   7 =
3 =   8 =
4 =   9 =

```
              L I F E
E.  MAN  ) G A L A X Y
           M A N
           M N L A
           L I G N
             L F A X
             L X L N
               L M X Y
               L L E N
                 L L Y
```

0 =   5 =
1 =   6 =
2 =   7 =
3 =   8 =
4 =   9 =

```
                 N O N R
F.  PULSAR  ) S U P E R N O V A
              R L L A O N
              U U P A V O
              P U L S A R
                L P S U A V
                R L L A O N
                  N P S L P E A
                  N V L E A P R
                    N E V E U L
```

0 =   5 =
1 =   6 =
2 =   7 =
3 =   8 =
4 =   9 =

Answers: page 98

VARIABLE STARS

Here's one for you variable star observers. The list at left gives pairs of stars having the same type of variation. Classifications are given at right. Can you identify the class to which each pair of stars belongs? Get them all and you should apply for membership in IAU Commission 25 (Variable Stars).

1. GK Per, T Aur   ____   a. RV Tauri stars
2. AR Aur, WW Aur   ____   b. Long period variables
3. AO Cas, UW CMa   ____   c. UV Ceti (flare) stars
4. SU Aur, GW Ori   ____   d. Novae
5. ER Ori, AH Vir   ____   e. Orion variables
6. SS Cyg, U Gem   ____   f. Beta Lyrae systems
7. U Sgr, S Sge   ____   g. Delta Scuti stars
8. X Ari, U Sex   ____   h. Eclipsing binaries similar to Algol
9. Epsilon Cep, Delta Del   ____   i. Dwarf novae
10. Gamma Peg, Beta Cep   ____   j. W Ursae Majoris systems
11. BL Her, UY Eri   ____   k. Beta Canis Majoris systems
12. BZ Sct, AR Sgr   ____   l. Classical Cepheids
13. V645 Cen, AD Leo   ____   m. RR Lyrae stars
14. S Cas, R Boo   ____   n. W Virginis stars

Answers: page 98

OBSERVATORIES

Ask any buff where Mount Wilson Observatory is located; the reply, "California," is immediate. Below are two dozen observatories whose locations are well-known, but can you identify them by their coordinates? Did you know, for example, that one of the westernmost observatories is _____ ?

		Longitude			Latitude		
		h	m	s	°	′	″
1. Arecibo	____	a. 5	19	20.7	+38	26	17
2. Boston University	____	b. 7	04	50.3	+39	23	29
3. Cincinnati	____	c. 4	27	00.7	+18	20	37
4. Fernbank Science Center	____	d. 5	37	16.3	+33	46	38
5. Flower and Cook	____	e. 8	08	37.7	+37	55	06
6. Goethe Link	____	f. 4	51	42.0	+41	18	58
7. G. R. Agassiz Station	____	g. 4	44	25.5	+42	21	01
8. Harvard College	____	h. 5	45	34.9	+39	32	58
9. High Altitude at Climax	____	i. 4	44	31.0	+42	22	48
10. Kitt Peak National	____	j. 5	37	41.4	+39	08	20
11. Leuschner	____	k. 5	26	16.4	+41	32	13
12. Lick	____	l. 5	32	13.3	+40	15	04
13. Lowell	____	m. 5	08	15.7	+38	55	17
14. McMath-Hulbert	____	n. 7	26	39.2	+35	12	06
15. Mount Wilson	____	o. 4	46	14.2	+42	30	13
16. National Radio Astronomy	____	p. 5	33	03.3	+42	39	48
17. Palomar	____	q. 8	06	34.9	+37	20	25
18. Perkins	____	r. 7	52	14.3	+34	13	00
19. Sproul	____	s. 7	47	27.4	+33	21	22
20. Steward at Tucson	____	t. 5	01	54.3	+39	59	57
21. United States Naval	____	u. 5	01	25.6	+39	54	16
22. Warner and Swasey	____	v. 7	26	22.7	+31	57	30
23. Yale University	____	w. 5	54	13.6	+42	34	13
24. Yerkes	____	x. 7	23	47.7	+32	13	59

Answers: page 98

CONSTELLATION NAMES

The constellations are named after many different things. Mythical and real animals are immortalized in the skies as are persons and occupations. Those listed below represent things. How many can you identify?

1.	Antlia	____	a.	Microscope
2.	Ara	____	b.	Furnace
3.	Caelum	____	c.	Octant
4.	Carina	____	d.	Pump
5.	Circinus	____	e.	Arrow
6.	Crater	____	f.	Ship's sails
7.	Fornax	____	g.	Ship's stern
8.	Horologium	____	h.	Altar
9.	Libra	____	i.	Pair of compasses
10.	Lyra	____	j.	Square
11.	Microscopium	____	k.	Easel
12.	Norma	____	l.	Sextant
13.	Octans	____	m.	Telescope
14.	Pictor	____	n.	Net
15.	Puppis	____	o.	Ship's compass
16.	Pyxis	____	p.	Harp
17.	Reticulum	____	q.	Balance
18.	Sagitta	____	r.	Cup
19.	Scutum	____	s.	Ship's keel
20.	Sextans	____	t.	Chisel
21.	Telescopium	____	u.	Clock
22.	Vela	____	v.	Shield

Answers: page 99

The Hour

INTELLIGENCE (?) TEST

1. From a TV Quiz Show: When can you see farther, during the day or during the night?

2. From *The Old Farmer's Almanac:* Make a single word from the expression NO MORE STARS.

3. Various: A hunter leaves his campsite and walks six miles due south. Following a quick lunch, he heads west four miles and shoots a bear. After skinning the bear, he heads north and returns to camp. What color was the bear?

4. You are observing Jupiter in the early evening sky and note the shadow of Ganymede crossing the planet's surface.
   a. Does the shadow precede or follow the disk of the satellite?
   b. In what direction is the shadow moving?

5. From *Astronomy* by Russell, Dugan, and Stewart: The battle of Princeton was fought on January 3, 1777. There was a solar eclipse on January 9. About what time did the moon rise on the night before the battle?

6. From *The Old Farmer's Almanac:* I am a word of four letters in which may be found *a.* a verb, *b.* an animal, *c.* a viscid liquid, *d.* a skill, *e.* a conjunction, and *f.* a preposition.

7. From a Harvard PhD qualifying examination about 1949: What is the significance of Mount Brukharus?

8. From an Indiana University qualifying examination about 1952: What is a gnomon?

9. From *The Old Farmer's Almanac:* Why is a hen immortal?

10. From *Astronomy* by Russell, Dugan, and Stewart: Will the ephemeris of the sun for one year be correct for every other year? If not, when did the maximum deviation occur and when will it occur again?

11. The volume of water in the oceans is estimated to be 328,750,000 cubic miles. Assume that the average, 150-pound person contains 100 pounds of water. It has been projected that by 1980 some 4×10^9 persons will inhabit this planet. At the time that projection was made, the Earth's population was doubling every 35 years. Should this rate continue, in how many years will the quantity of water within people equal the current amount of water in the oceans?

12. Identify the author of:
    a. *Twinkle, twinkle, little star,*   b. *Twinkle, twinkle, little bat!*
    How I wonder what you are,   *How I wonder what you're at!*
    Up above the world so high,   *Up above the world you fly*
    Like a diamond in the sky.   *Like a teatray in the sky.*

13. Extra credit on a Tufts University examination: Who was Jepp?

14. Even more trivia: What is the alleged cause of death of Tycho's pet elk?

15. Listed below are six types of years that differ somewhat in length; rearrange them in the order shortest to longest:
Anomalistic, Eclipse, Gregorian, Julian, Sidereal, Tropical.

16. What, besides astronomy, was Edwin P. Hubble's favorite passtime?

17. What contemporary astronomer might be appropriately introduced as "The beard that made Milwaukee famous"?

18. The distance to Sirius is more than a million million million gigaangstroms. True or false?

19. Are there more named or designated variable stars in Sagittarius (as of the middle of 1978) than naked-eye stars in the entire sky?

20. Which of Canopus, Crux, or the Large Magellanic Cloud would you have to go farthest south from northern latitudes to see?

21. What was the name that William Herschel gave to Uranus?
Who suggested that Uranus be used instead?

22. What contemporary astronomer includes dolphins among his friends?

23. The total mass of the satellites of all the planets is more than 100 times the total estimated mass of all the asteroids. True or false?

24. The starlight from the whole sky is equivalent to the light of 230 stars of zero photographic magnitude. How many fifth–magnitude stars would be required to produce a similar amount of light?

25. What constellation has the greatest area in terms of square degrees?

26. The Bay of Fundy is famous for its very high tides. On a recent cruise to that area a couple left their boat anchored and climbed over the side on a rope ladder to their dinghy. They noted that the bottom rung of the ladder just rested on the top of the water. While they were gone, the tide rose six feet. If the rungs on the ladder were one foot apart, how many were covered when they returned to the boat?

27. Six graduate students plan to measure the height of the tower of the McMath Solar Telescope on Kitt Peak. They decide on an antique mercury barometer as an appropriate instrument. Each agrees to use a different method. What ways can you think of?

28. An astronomer has discovered a rather interesting phenomenon. When he wore his hat, jacket, boots, and gloves, a certain variable star took 0.10125 day to go through its light cycle; when he re-

moved his hat, the cycle took 8,748 seconds; when hat and gloves were removed, the cycle lasted 2.43 hours; and without his hat, gloves, and jacket, the cycle was only 145.8 minutes. Can you explain?

29. Four astronomers were sitting around a card table. One was in the midst of dealing a hand of bridge when a night assistant called to say that it looked as though the sky was clearing. All immediately rose and went outside to see. It was a false alarm. They returned to the table and took their same seats, but none could remember who had been dealt the last card. "Don't bother counting," said the dealer, who was obviously experienced in these situations, "It will come out all right and each of you will have the cards you should." He continued to deal. How?

30. Today there are 88 recognized constellations. But in an old astronomy text, 98 are identified. From among the constellations listed here can you identify those that no longer exist? Air Pump, Bird of Paradise, Hadley's Quadrant, Pair of Compasses, Goose, Sculptor's Tools, Mariner's Compass.

31. Which is the longest season in the Southern Hemisphere?

32. From the North Pole is it usually possible to observe a total solar eclipse during the winter? What about a total lunar eclipse?

33. From whom would you buy products bearing the following names:
   a. Comet   d. Quasar   h. Polaris
   b. Venus   e. Milky Way   i. Nova
   c. Mars   f. Galaxy   j. Jupiter
                 g. Mercury

34. The names of a large genus of acquatic herbs, a superfamily of raptorial birds with only one species, and a constellation are all derived from the same Latin word. It is _____.

35. Missed that one? How about a polyp that also shares its name with a constellation?

Answers: pages 99 and 100

Day and Night

ASTEROID NETWORK

Names of the first 100 asteroids to be discovered, grouped by the number of letters in each, are given below. These are to be fitted into the network on the facing page so that all the names link. Since there are only two asteroids represented by names containing two or eleven letters, no starting clue is provided.

Two letters:

IO

Four letters:

ASIA DIKE ECHO HEBE IRIS ISIS JUNO KLIO LEDA LETO MAJA NYSA

Five letters:

AEGLE CERES CIRCE DANAE DIANA DORIS ELPIS ERATO FIDES FLORA FREIA IRENE JULIA METIS NIOBE PALES VESTA

Six letters:

AEGINA AGLAJA AURORA CYBELE DAPHNE EGERIA EUROPA FRIGGA HEKATE HESTIA HYGIEA IANTHE KLOTHO KLYTIA MELETE PALLAS POMONA PSYCHE SAPPHO SEMELE SYLVIA THALIA THEMIS THETIS THISBE UNDINA URANIA

Seven letters:

ALKMENE ANTIOPE ARIADNE ASTRAEA AUSONIA BEATRIX BELLONA EUGENIA EUNOMIA EUTERPE FERONIA FORTUNA GALATEA KALYPSO LUTETIA MINERVA NEMAUSA PANDORA PHOCAEA

Eight letters:

ANGELINA ARETHUSA ATALANTE EURYDIKE EURYNOME HARMONIA HESPERIA KALLIOPE LAETITIA MASSALIA PANOPAEA VICTORIA VIRGINIA

Nine letters:

ALEXANDRA CONCORDIA LEUKOTHEA MELPOMENE MNEMOSYNE

Ten letters:

AMPHITRITE EUPHROSYNE PARTHENOPE POLYHYMNIA PROSERPINA

Eleven letters:

TERPSICHORE

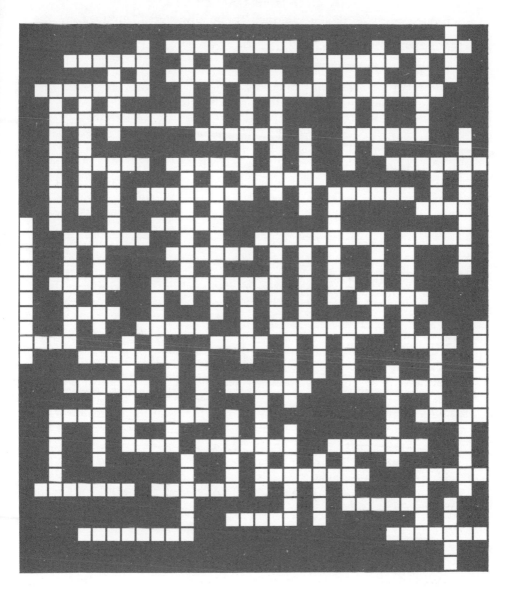

Answers: page 101

If the night is really bad, maybe you would like to verify the following problem taken from E. Burritt's *The Geography of the Heavens*, 1838 edition.

Problem XIV is "to find the distance of any planet from the sun, that of the earth being known," in accordance with the rule:

> Divide the square of the planet's [period of] sidereal revolution round the Sun, by the square of the Earth's sidereal revolution, and multiply the cube root of the quotient by the Earth's mean distance from the Sun.

As an example, the author calculates the mean distance of Mercury from the sun as follows: "Mercury's sidereal revolution is 87.969258 days, or 7600543^S.8912: The Earth's sidereal revolution is 365.256374417 days, or

31558151^S.5	7600543^S.9
31558151^S.5	7600543^S.9

995916962096952.25 *   by which divide   57768267575827.21

and the quotient will be 0.052005106713292,* the cube root of which is 0.3870977, and this multiplied by 94,881,891, gives 36,727,607 miles, for Mercury's distance from the Sun."

To verify the above arithmetic, it is totally unfair to use a calculator. In fact, the author continues, "This problem may be performed by logarithms in as many *minutes* [his emphasis] as the former method requires *hours.*"

As a footnote, it's rather curious that in the logarithmic treatment the author uses 95,273,869 miles for the earth's mean distance from the sun and derives a result for Mercury of 36,880,422 miles. Without noticing the discrepancy he then raves about the use of logarithms and concludes, "He need not think himself a *dull* scholar, if by the former method he come to the true result in *five hours;* nor remarkably quick, if by the latter he come to it in *five minutes.*" Can you do this problem longhand in under five hours?

---

*The quote is exact. However, I find the square of the earth's sidereal period to be 995916926096952.25 (the italicized numbers were seemingly transposed in typesetting). And my calculator indicates the quotient to be .058005 .... Strangely, Burritt's derived cube root corresponds to my quotient, not his. It seems that his book had at least two typographical errors! How many more can you find?

WHO OBSERVES WHICH PLANET?

In the village of Oldee Townee there is an active astronomical society with eight members: Mr. Mercury, Ms. Venus, Mr. Mars, Mr. Jupiter, Mr. Saturn, Mr. Uranus, Mr. Neptune, and Mr. Pluto. Each member, and only that member, observes one planet of the solar system. No member observes the planet that bears his or her name.

It has been determined that:

1. Mercury's observer sends his observations to the *Astrophysical Journal* and Mars' observer has sent his to *Sky and Telescope*.

2. Mr. Neptune observes four satellites belonging to his planet.

3. The heavenly namesakes of the observers of Venus and Neptune are neighbors in the solar system.

4. Jupiter is outside his observer's heavenly namesake's orbit.

5. Mr. Saturn has no interest in Neptune. Five years ago he mistook Venus for his planet and has since then given up observing in disgust.

6. Ms. Venus and Mr. Jupiter observe neighboring planets.

7 Mr. Pluto is building a telescope and hopes it will be ready for the next opposition of his planet.

8. Ms. Venus has delved into the archival records to consult Sir William Herschel's observations of her planet.

Which observer observes which planet? Hints are on page 89.

This is a slight variation on a puzzle that first appeared in *The Observatory* (1934).

Answers: page 101

THE SCAFFOLDING IS VERY NICE, BUT WHERE IS THE TELESCOPE?

PHYSICAL EXERCISE

Having gained some local notoriety by estimating the number of snowflakes that fell on metropolitan Boston during the giant storm of February, 1978 — or at least coming the closest to the answer that some machine had turned up for a local television station — Jack Tessman, who teaches "Physics for Humanists" at Tufts University, provided some additional food for thought during a recent spring semester.

1. The General Electric Company provided him with 7,000 rejected light bulbs all of the same size. From a bar supported at both ends, a pair of light bulbs was suspended by threads of equal length, with the bulbs in contact. The whole contraption was placed at the entrance to the Engineering School Library with a large container below to collect the debris. Students, faculty, and staff were invited to come by and break light bulbs simply by letting one swing against the other.

> a. What law of physics was Professor Tessman trying to prove?
>
> b What do you think the results showed?

2. In a separate undertaking, Professor Tessman decided to find out what would happen if grass were grown on a rotating turntable. Grass seed was planted in a container that was attached to a disk driven by an electric motor.

> a. Which way did the grass grow?
>
> b. Why?

Answers: page 102

THE ABSENT-MINDED ASTRONOMERS
(Reprinted from *The Observatory*, 1936)

When the Greenbridge expedition returned from the total eclipse of the Sun in 1899 at Addis Ababa, the instruments were put away, and were not examined for some years afterwards. It appeared later that a quartz spectrograph was missing, and since the records of this eclipse expedition were singularly incomplete, it was necessary to question the four senior members of the Greenbridge Observatory staff. Each was asked four questions, and each old gentleman had made three correct replies and one incorrect reply. The replies were as follows:

Professor Apple: 1. Beans went to this eclipse.
2. Carrots was using a flint spectrograph.
3. Doughnut was delivering lectures in the U.S.A. at the time.
4. I was in Africa at the time in question.

Sir B. Beans: 1. I have never bean to any eclipse.
2. Doughnut was not in Africa.
3. Carrots was not using a quartz spectrograph.
4. Apple was in Potsdam.

Dr. Carrots: 1. Beans has never used a quartz spectrograph.
2. Doughnut was present at the eclipse.
3. I used a flint spectrograph.
4. Apple was not in Germany.

Mr. Doughnut: 1. I have never been to an eclipse.
2. Apple went to that eclipse.
3. I was in U.S.A. at the time.
4. Carrots had the quartz spectrograph.

Which of them did use the quartz spectrograph?

Answer: page 102

Moon (Monday)
*Gypsy Planet and
Dream Book*

— 29 —

TELESCOPE ALLOCATIONS

From a certain perspective, one can see five domes in a straight line. Each contains a telescope of a different aperture; each telescope is used by a visiting astronomer from a different state. Each astronomer has a particular drink and a particular way of dealing with tobacco that he or she prefers. In addition, each astronomer has run across a particular form of wildlife on the mountaintop.

The visitor from Kansas was amazed to see lady bugs swarming all through the dome of the telescope assigned to him. The 16-inch telescope is used by the Louisiana astronomer. While the Hoosier astronomer quaffs Coca-Cola, the user of the 36-inch drinks copious amounts of coffee. The dome of the 36-inch, incidentally, is immediately to the right of the 84-inch telescope's dome. The cigarette smoker has problems with field mice. The pipe smoker is scheduled on the 150-inch. After the night is over, the astronomer assigned to the middle telescope relaxes with a glass of brandy. The Massachusetts visitor uses the telescope in the first dome. The astronomer who chews tobacco works next to the one who found a tarantula on the observing platform. The pipe smoker uses the telescope in the dome next to the one in which a nest of scorpions was found. Coors is the favorite drink of the cigar smoker. The Texan uses snuff. The astronomer from Massachusetts works next to the 50-inch dome.

1. Who drinks Lemonade?
2. Who stepped over a rattlesnake?

This problem has appeared in a variety of places and in a variety of forms.

Hints: page 90   Answers: page 102

AN UNSOLVED PUZZLE

R. H. Allen, in his *Star-Names and Their Meanings*, has this to say about Alpha and Beta Delphini: "The strange names **Sualocin** and **Rotanev** first appeared for these stars in [G. Piazzi's] *Palermo Catalogue* of 1814, and long were a mystery to all.... [T. W.] Webb, however, discovered their origin by reversing the component letters, and so reading *Nicolaus Venator*, the Latinized form of Niccolo Cacciatore, the name of the assistant and successor of Piazzi."

The *Palermo Catalogue* also contains another strange name, **Iclarkrav** for Delta Scorpii, for which no satisfactory explanation has ever been found. Assuming that it, too, is some kind of an anagram, whose name is concealed here?

SIGNS AND SYMBOLS

Arranged below are the various planetary symbols and zodiacal signs in common usage. How many can you identify?

1.	♂	_____	A.	Aquarius
2.	♑	_____	B.	Pluto
3.	♆	_____	C.	Taurus
4.	♋	_____	D.	Capricornus
5.	♃	_____	E.	Sun
6.	♍	_____	F.	Leo
7.	♐	_____	G.	Scorpio
8.	♅	_____	H.	Moon
9.	♀	_____	I.	Neptune
10.	♏	_____	J.	Mars
11.	☽	_____	K.	Virgo
12.	♊	_____	L.	Aries
13.	♎	_____	M.	Earth
14.	♄	_____	N.	Cancer
15.	♒	_____	O.	Mercury
16.	♇	_____	P.	Gemini
17.	♉	_____	Q.	Uranus
18.	☉	_____	R.	Sagittarius
19.	♈	_____	S.	Libra
20.	☿	_____	T.	Pisces
21.	⊕	_____	U.	Saturn
22.	♌	_____	V.	Venus
23.	♓	_____	W.	Jupiter

Answers: page 102

The Week

— 31 —

ATOMIC COMPOSITION OF CONSTELLATIONS

Bet you never thought that certain constellations have a definite atomic composition. Take PAVO, for example. It is composed of protactinium plus vanadium and oxygen. How do I know? Well, the atomic symbols for these elements are, in order, Pa, V, O; thus, PA + V + O = PAVO. Actually, it is probably easier to start with the reverse. In the first six cases below, identify the constellation that has the given atomic composition. Then see how well you can do in determining the composition of the remaining half dozen. If you need help, hints are provided on page 90.

1. Boron + Oxygen + Oxygen + Tellurium + Sulphur
2. Chromium + Astatine + Erbium
3. Lutetium + Plutonium + Sulphur
4. Tantalum + Uranium + Ruthenium + Sulphur
5. Lanthanum + Carbon + Erbium + Tantalum
6. Carbon + Argon + Iodine + Sodium
7. CIRCINUS
8. LIBRA
9. MONOCEROS
10. OCTANS
11. PISCES
12. PUPPIS

Answers: page 102

MESSIER CATALOGUE

How well do you know the Messier Catalogue? Listed below are 15 Messier objects that you should be able to match up with the common names in the column at right. Less than 12 correct? — go back to your Norton's *Star Atlas*.

M1 _____   a. Whirlpool nebula
M8 _____   b. Dumbbell nebula
M13 _____   c. Sombrero nebula
M17 _____   d. Andromeda nebula
M20 _____   e. Crab nebula
M27 _____   f. Blackeye nebula
M31 _____   g. Trifid nebula
M42 _____   h. Hercules cluster
M44 _____   i. Pleiades cluster
M45 _____   j. Owl nebula
M51 _____   k. Lagoon nebula
M57 _____   l. Praesepe or Beehive cluster
M64 _____   m. Ring nebula
M97 _____   n. Omega or Horseshoe nebula
M104 _____   o. Great Nebula in Orion

Answers: page 103

CONSTELLATION OVERLAPS

In a number of instances the last two letters in a constellation's name are the same as the first two letters in the name of another. These overlap letters are given below. Can you identify all the constellations? Some problems have alternative answers.

1. _ _ _ _ _ ER _ _ _ _ _ _ _ _
2. _ _ VO _ _ _ _ _
3. _ _ _ _ _ _ _ _ _ _ _ CI _ _ _ _ _ _ _
4. _ _ _ _ _ LA _ _ _ _ _ _
5. _ _ _ _ _ _ TA _ _ _ _ _
6. _ _ _ _ CO _ _ _ _ _
7. _ LE _
8. _ _ _ _ CA _ _ _ _ _
9. _ _ _ _ _ _ _ _ OR _ _ _ _
10. _ _ _ _ SA _ _ _ _ _ _ _ _ _ _

Answers: page 103

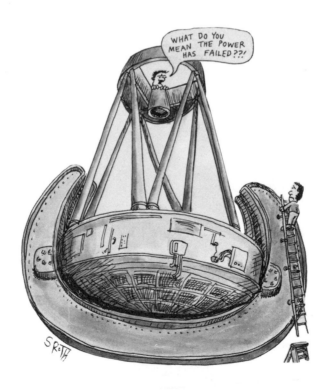

STAR NAME OVERLAPS

Below are given the last two or three letters in the proper name of a star that correspond to the first two or three in the name of another. You should have no problem in identifying the first few, but the remainder are quite obscure unless you really know your star names and their variations. Standard designations are given on page 90.

1. _ _ _ C A _ _ _ _ _ _
2. _ _ _ _ _ _ C A _ _ _ _ _
3. _ _ _ A L _ _ _ _ _ _
4. _ _ _ _ _ _ A R _ _ _ _ _ _
5. _ _ _ _ _ _ _ _ S E _ _ _ _ _ _
6. _ _ _ A L _ _ _
7. _ _ C O R _ _ _ _ _ _ _
8. _ _ _ _ _ T H _ _ _ _ _
9. _ _ _ _ _ _ _ S H _ _ _ _
10. _ _ _ A R _ _ _ _
11. _ _ _ _ _ _ A R _ _ _
12. _ _ _ S A _ _
13. _ _ P H _ _ _ _
14. _ _ _ _ _ C H _ _ _
15. _ _ _ R A _ _ _ _ _ _ _
16. _ _ _ P H _ _ _ _ _
17. _ _ _ _ _ _ B A _ _ _
18. _ _ _ _ T A _ _ _ _ _ _
19. _ _ _ _ _ N A _ _ _ _ _
20. _ _ _ _ R A _ _ _ _ _ _ _ _

Answers: page 103

Mars (Tuesday)
*Gypsy Planet and
Dream Book*

WHAT THEY ARE REMEMBERED FOR

The association of the name in the left column with an item in the right leads to a well-defined term that should be contained in most any astronomical glossary. First, identify the terms; then get a piece of paper and define them. If your results match mine you are well on the way to your PhD!

1.	Alfvén	—	a.	constant
2.	Avogadro	—	b.	prism
3.	Balmer	—	c.	razor
4.	Barnard	—	d.	gaps
5.	Bok	—	e.	galaxy
6.	Cassini	—	f.	waves
7.	Chandrasekhar	—	g.	radius
8.	Compton	—	h.	bands
9.	Coulomb	—	i.	comet
10.	Doppler	—	j.	diagram
11.	Ekman	—	k.	series
12.	Faraday	—	l.	black hole
13.	Fermi	—	m.	sphere
14.	Gould	—	n.	paradox
15.	Golay	—	o.	effect
16.	Halley	—	p.	Observatory
17.	Hubble	—	q.	number
18.	Johnson	—	r.	collision
19.	Kelvin	—	s.	lobe
20.	Kepler	—	t.	camera
21.	Kerr	—	u.	layer
22.	Kirkwood	—	v.	star
23.	Lemaitre	—	w.	noise
24.	Lallemand	—	x.	parameters
25.	Lowell	—	y.	scale
26.	Maksutov	—	z.	globule
27.	Mie	—	A.	universe
28.	Nicol	—	B.	instability
29.	Ockham	—	C.	clouds
30.	Olbers	—	D.	cell
31.	Oort	—	E.	scattering

32.	Rankine	—	F. limit
33.	Roche	—	G. laws
34.	Schwarzschild	—	H. telescope
35.	Seyfert	—	I. belt
36.	Stokes	—	J. gas
37.	Strömgren	—	K. contraction
38.	Swan	—	L. shift
39.	Taylor	—	M. division
40.	Wolf	—	N. rotation

Answers: pages 103 and 104

SUN WORDS

Although it is a cloudy night, maybe tomorrow will be sunny. Below are 21 words that contain the letters *S U N*. Fill in the missing letters to produce the words defined by the expressions on the right. If you get them all, you deserve only clear nights. Par for the course is 17.

A. _ S U N _ _ _ _ _   capital of Paraguay
B. S U N _ _ _ _ _ _   expose the body to the sun
C. S U N _ _ _ _ _   overexposure!
D. S U N _ _ _ _   fallen in
E. S U N _ _ _ _ _ _   type of feldspar
F. _ _ _ S U N   foreign car
G. S U N _ _ _ _ _ _ _ _   astronomers shouldn't drink them
H. S U N _ _ _ _ _   but they can eat these
I. S U N _ _ _ _ _   won't tell time when it's raining
J. S U N _ _   body of traditional Moslem law
K. S U N _ _ _ _ _ _ _ _ _   way to have eggs
L. S U N _ _ _ _ _ _   miscellaneous items
M. S U N _   tropical plant
N. S U N _ _ _ _   plant whose leaves have sticky hairs
O. S U N _ _ _ _ _ _   state flower of Kansas
P. S U N _ _ _ _ _   fun sail boat
Q. S U N _ _   strait that connects Java Sea
                              with Indian Ocean
R. S U N _ _ _   cheerful
S. _ _ S U N   in charge of deck crew
T. S U N _ _ _ _   break apart
U. S U N _ _ _ _ _   home of Sacramento Peak Observatory

Answers: page 104

The Month

AN EVENING WITH WILLIAM SHAKESPEARE

I was perched on a rock watching the sun set when suddenly I heard a voice behind me exclaim:

"Hung be the Heavens with black, yield day to night!"   1. ____

I spun around, and there stood a man of medium height dressed in a black velvet suit. The knickers, the high collar, the floppy hat all suggested a person headed to a fancy dress ball. "Don't be startled," the apparition said, "the name's Shakespeare, Will Shakespeare."

"But, Mr. Shakespeare," I started to say . . . .

"Call me Will," he interrupted.

"O.K. But Will, how did you get here? You've been dead for centuries."

"Oh," he replied, "I sometimes drop in on

This earth of majesty, this seat of Mars   2. ____

to catch up with what you astronomers are doing."

"This is the earth, but I would hardly call it the 'seat of Mars'."

"Be that as it may," he rejoined, "my memory is pretty good. I remember all the lines I ever wrote, but I have trouble identifying the play in which they first appeared. Maybe you can help me."

"Very interesting," I said, "but why are you so concerned with what astronomers are up to."

"Well, since I last came by, you have found quasars, pulsars, and X-ray binaries, but

There are more things in heaven and earth, Horatio
Than are dreamt of in your philosophy."   3. ____

"My name's not Horatio, but I certainly agree that there are some wonderful things up there."

"Yes," he commented, "there is remarkable order,

The heavens themselves, the planets, and this center
Observe degree, priority, and place,
Insisture, course, proportion, season, form,
Office, and custom, in all line of order."   4. ____

"Stick around," I said, "I swear by the moon ..."

"O!" he interrupted,

"O! swear not by the moon, the inconstant moon,
That monthly changes in her circled orb."   5. ____

"All right, I won't. But as soon as it is dark, I'll show you some things."

"Ah," said he,

"The moon is down,"   6. ____

"The bright day is done,
And we are for the dark."   7. ____

I rose to go, but was stopped.

"*Sit, Jessica* [another memory lapse]. *Look how the floor of heaven*
        Is thick inlaid with patines of bright gold;
        There's not the smallest orb which thou behold'st."   8. _____

We dallied a moment longer, then headed for the nearby dome. When we reached the observing platform, he exclaimed upon seeing the telescope,   "*the glass of fashion and the mould of form,*
        The Observ'd of all observers."   9. _____

I switched off the dome lights and thought I heard him mutter
        "*This is the night*
        That either makes me or fordoes me quite."   10. _____

"What did you say?" I asked.

"Nothing, important," he responded, "just something I picked up from Bill Herschel or one of his graduate students. But, more to the point, as all now know,

        The instruments of darkness tell us truths."   11. _____

For the next few minutes I busied myself setting on the eclipsing novalike variable EX Hydrae. Will asked if he could look. I relinquished my place at the eyepiece and moved aside. While he was observing, I flicked on my flashlight to check the finding chart. Accidentally, the beam swung across his face, causing him to yell,

        "*Out damned spot! Out, I say!*"   12. _____

"Sorry about that, Will."

Everything was finally in order; dark slides were pulled; the recorder activated. We stood back to observe on the chart the rapid brightness changes of the star. Will commented,

        "*The moist star*
        Upon whose influence Neptune's empire stands
Is [he slightly changed this word] *sick almost to doomsday with eclipse.*"
                                                    13. _____

After a while he seemed to lose interest and wandered off. I heard the door slam shut. Shortly it slammed again, and he came running up to stairs. "Come quickly. I was just outside,

        And certain stars shot madly from their spheres."   14. _____

"What do you mean?" I asked.

"Well, I saw at least one,
            . . . a shooting star
        Fall to the base earth from firmament.   15. _____

But you'd really better come outside for

        This night me thinks is but the daylight sick."   16. _____

Outside we went. It was true. Faint, whitish cirrus streaked the sky. At some points the clouds were thicker.

"Looks pretty bad," I commented. "But we can still see Rigel, Sirius, Bellatrix...."

"Ah, yes," he interjected, "in my wanderings I have met all of

> Those earthly godfathers of heaven's lights
>> that give a name to every fixed star."   17. ____

He paused, then pointed towards the Pleiades, "look

> Sometimes we see a cloud that's dragonish,   18. ____

the stars are about to be eaten."

Indeed, it did look as though the entire cluster was to be devoured.

We returned to the dome. I poured a cup of coffee and sat back to wait for the clouds to move in or out. He paced around, then out of the clear blue asked

> "What doth gravity out of his bed at midnight?"   19. ____

Answering his own question, he said, "Of course,

> That ebb and flow by the moon,   20. ____

the tides are with us day and night."

"That's certainly part of the answer," I commented.

He paced the floor some more. "There's a question I want to ask you," he finally said. "Do you believe that

> The stars above us govern our condition?"   21. ____

"No," I replied, "I certainly doubt that!"

"What!" he exclaimed. Only then, as he launched on a tirade, did I realize that I had hit a soft spot. "Doubt thou that

> Two stars keep not their motion in one sphere   22. ____

> Doubt thou the stars are fire
> Doubt that the sun doth move."   23. ____

"Wait a minute," I said, "calm down! You're getting ideas confused. You're right, the moon does have influence." But Will continued,

> "It is the very error of the moon;
> She comes more near the earth than she was wont
>> And makes men mad."   24. ____

"Frankly, I don't believe that either."

This triggered another dramatic outburst, but I finally was able to calm him down. He doffed his cap, ran a hand through thinning hair and sighed

> "O, I have passed a miserable night."   25. ____

"I'm sorry Will," I said, trying to think of some way to mollify him. "I don't really mean to doubt everything you believe in, and in fact I don't.

I bet you have something interesting to say about comets."

He grinned from ear to ear. "Ah comets, comets,

> *When beggars die, there are no comets seen;*
> *The heavens themselves blaze forth the death of princes."* **26.** ____

I bit my tongue.

The night was coming to an end. I stowed the telescope, closed the dome, and out we went into the early morning. In the east, Mercury was rising.

"That's my next stop," said Will as he took leave of me,

> *"A station like the herald Mercury*
> *New-lighted on a heaven-kissing hill."* **27.** ____

Getting into the spirit of things, I observed that

> *"Night's candles are burnt out, and jocund day*
> *Stands tiptoe on the misty mountaintops.* **28.** ____

So long, Will, don't change."

"Some might," he replied,

> *"But I am constant as the northern star,*
> *Of whose true-fix'd and resting quality*
> *There is no fellow in the firmament."* **29.** ____

Will's quotations are from the following plays; some have contributed more than one.

A. *Antony and Cleopatra*
B. *Hamlet*
C. *Henry IV*
D. *Henry VI*
E. *Julius Caesar*
F. *King Lear*
G. *Love's Labour's Lost*
H. *Macbeth*

I. *Merchant of Venice*
J. *Midsummer Night's Dream*
K. *Othello*
L. *Richard II*
M. *Richard III*
N. *Romeo and Juliet*
O. *Troilus and Cressida*

Answers: page 105

The Year

Search Games

The most common version of these games is to supply you with a list of words that you are expected to find in the adjacent maze of letters. The words are hidden through a variety of devices: they may run from top to bottom or bottom to top; left to right or right to left; and diagonally from upper to lower or lower to upper, either left or right. In addition, words may overlap. The sole stipulation is that letters must be adjacent to each other.

So much for the traditional way. In the searches presented here, we have generally added an additional feature. The particular names you are looking for are not given specifically, though most are alluded to in one way or another. After you have deduced the names, you will be asked to make further associations with them. If you need help, on pages 91 and 92 we have provided some "hints," the names of what you should be searching for.

Familiar Stars. Below are the common designations for 16 stars with familiar names, all of which appear among the letters in the matrix on this page. First find all the star names; then match them with the designations. The names you are looking for are given on page 91.

A. α Aql
B. α CMa
C. α Car
D. α Cen C

E. o Cet
F. α Cyg
G. α Gem
H. β Gem

I. α Lyr
J. α Ori
K. β Ori
L. γ Ori

M. β Per
N. α Sco
O. 28 Tau
P. α UMi

```
A C H I S U R I A L B E L L R S M N O
P M I T E R C L A H S T A L T A R R P
H N I R S Y K A W V E G A A G L E R O
O L V R T R R E P F N M X S T A O S T
B C A R A M N F E T A U I A D X Y U U
R S O L N L I F E L L V P E I W K I L
A S D E T Y Y C A L O L R M W E M R N
X A E R A M N O O P C F A N R S A I A
E H N S R N L P L O A C A N O P U S Y
A B E T E L G E U S E E U S E A P B A
A B B F S L M M O N P N P T C S V X W
B E E H N E L A T Y G R O O U I X E A
V A L T T G M A S R Y B L I M R A C L
O X L U L I U C A S T O R Y E A B P S
T A A F D R V N L P O T A A X L V M I
E T T S I C O P G O G O L P A O P I N
B C R F P D L M O N I R I U U P S S T
A E I A S R I A L T A I R L A L I N O
X A X I I O L N M T T R O I A N M R S
H C A E U R U I S A H N M W T R E C F
```

Answers: page 105

Ushi (The Ox)
Japanese Zodiac
from *Family Crests*

Satellite Search. Another two-part quiz. The names of 29 satellites of various planets are hidden within the maze of letters below. How many can you find? To complicate matters, the name of one satellite occurs at least eight times. After you have found all the satellites, match them with their planets. An alphabetical listing of the satellites appears on page 91.

```
A  C  D  F  A  E  L  Q  P  R  P  O  Z  M  N  I  M  N
W  P  E  P  H  E  N  P  O  S  Y  O  U  F  P  S  Z  Q
I  P  O  S  N  D  L  H  S  S  A  L  L  T  H  L  E  S
E  S  T  S  A  J  L  O  K  T  U  R  H  D  E  N  T  O
T  W  S  U  D  A  L  E  C  N  E  R  E  I  D  H  E  N
E  N  I  N  N  X  B  T  P  D  A  R  B  E  G  E  A
S  R  L  S  A  U  T  E  R  H  E  A  A  N  Q  R  S  A
R  T  L  N  R  S  A  E  N  O  M  S  A  M  I  M  T  T
H  E  A  M  I  P  T  L  H  H  Y  P  E  R  I  O  N  R
P  U  C  Q  M  E  O  I  G  H  N  Z  Z  W  N  O  N  L
E  W  H  I  M  H  E  S  T  I  A  C  H  V  G  N  U  W
E  H  O  E  P  E  Y  E  E  A  G  O  U  W  I  L  L  F
I  N  D  E  N  T  T  F  E  I  N  D  E  R  T  A  I  N
I  N  G  A  E  U  R  O  P  A  D  I  N  D  U  E  Q  U
A  L  L  Y  A  S  I  A  F  E  A  O  A  N  M  Z  N  L
I  G  H  T  E  H  T  D  N  P  I  N  N  B  O  Q  G
A  S  T  H  I  H  O  E  E  S  H  E  F  Z  R  W  P  O
N  E  W  E  H  A  N  T  O  I  D  O  B  E  I  Y  E  P
E  Y  O  U  F  O  U  U  N  D  M  N  B  N  E  Y  O  T
R  A  T  H  E  S  R  T  O  B  N  O  P  O  L  E  S  T
O  F  R  E  T  T  E  L  R  M  R  S  S  G  S  N  Q  W
Y  D  S  E  F  P  O  M  N  O  S  T  R  E  A  G  O  L
```

Answers: page 106

Tatsu (The Dragon)
Japanese Zodiac
from *Family Crests*

Observatory Search. Names of 22 observatories, whose locations are given below, are hidden among the letters in the matrix. The object is to match each observatory with its location. Try finding all the observatories before turning to page 91 where they are listed alphabetically.

A. Albany, New York
B. Bloomington, Indiana
C. Boulder, Colorado
D. Cedar Rapids, Iowa
E. Charlottesville, Virginia
F. Columbus, Ohio
G. Decatur, Georgia
H. Evanston, Illinois
I. Fayette, Missouri
J. Hanover, New Hampshire
K. Haverford, Pennsylvania

L. Madison, Wisconsin
M. Middletown, Connecticut
N. Riverside, Maryland
O. Nantucket, Massachusetts
P. Northfield, Minnesota
Q. Oakland, California
R. Portage Lake, Michigan
S. Providence, Rhode Island
T. Scottsdale, Arizona
U. Sunspot, New Mexico
V. Wilmington, Delaware

```
J  B  K  A  V  N  E  R  R  U  I  Z  W  A  K  U  L  O  P  M
I  C  A  X  C  V  A  R  L  W  E  S  S  I  L  O  O  L  L  P
A  D  E  A  R  B  O  R  N  M  H  R  R  D  D  U  D  L  E  Y
Q  V  P  E  T  A  O  I  N  A  S  K  H  R  D  L  G  U  A  O
B  A  O  F  G  K  M  R  T  A  W  S  Y  O  U  T  O  I  N  S
X  N  T  S  B  X  V  T  U  O  C  V  B  N  T  T  O  A  D  E
O  V  N  X  C  V  U  J  O  I  B  F  I  C  F  A  D  K  E  L
I  L  E  X  Z  C  F  D  O  B  R  A  D  L  E  Y  S  Q  R  A
V  E  M  B  K  R  F  D  O  C  T  V  H  A  A  P  E  X  M  M
V  C  A  X  C  O  I  B  X  N  T  U  N  C  T  V  L  V  C  O
D  K  R  W  A  S  H  B  U  R  N  N  C  E  H  O  L  P  C  A
E  R  C  O  P  A  R  O  U  I  M  X  S  C  E  T  A  E  O  P
Q  M  A  R  I  A  M  I  T  C  H  E  L  L  R  A  E  K  R  A
C  V  S  X  I  Y  N  I  L  L  I  M  C  M  R  M  C  A  M  I
B  A  C  T  M  A  R  Y  L  A  N  D  P  O  I  N  T  L  I  O
V  C  U  M  O  R  R  I  S  O  N  X  C  L  D  F  A  E  C  L
I  V  U  O  I  A  E  I  O  U  A  E  A  V  G  G  E  G  K  M
X  M  O  U  N  T  C  U  B  A  I  D  C  E  E  F  Q  A  S  T
L  A  I  R  O  M  E  M  E  G  D  I  R  B  W  A  R  T  S  S
A  E  I  O  U  T  K  L  M  M  L  K  T  A  I  U  N  R  M  R
A  E  I  T  H  C  S  U  A  B  S  R  E  M  M  O  S  O  L  L
D  E  S  T  E  A  B  G  I  Y  U  T  H  N  N  M  P  P  S  V
A  S  W  W  A  B  M  N  K  L  P  P  S  R  T  Y  Y  U  A  V
```

Answers: page 107

Lunar features.   Below are some very brief descriptions of the lunar features whose names are in the maze on the next page. First find the features, then match them with the descriptions. Hints are on page 91.

A. Moutain range bordering Mare Imbrium on southwest.
B. Mountain range between Mare Imbrium and Mare Serenitatis.
C. Walled-plain, 145 miles in diameter.
D. Walled-plain, one of the darkest on the moon.
E. Walled-plain, 100 miles across with ruined walls.
F. Isolated mountain on Mare Imbrium.
G. Crater, 70 miles in diameter with 7,000-foot central mountain.
H. Crater, 32 miles in diameter with 15,000-foot walls on west and 7,600-foot walls on east.
I. Crater, 55 miles in diameter on northern border of Mare Humorum.
J. Crater, 120 miles in diameter close to limb.
K. Crater, 30 miles in diameter.
L. Crater, 40 miles in diameter at center of a ray system.
M. Crater, 30 miles in diameter, between Mare Serenitatis and Mare Tranquillitatis.
N. Crater, 80 miles in diameter with many craterlets.
O. Crater, most prominent at full moon.
P. Crater, 50 miles in diameter with broken walls.
Q. Crater, small with smooth interior.
R. Valley, 80 miles long through the Alps.
S. Crater, just east of item A.

LUNAR   ECLIPSE   PHENOMENON   S.Roth

```
S  U  A  S  B  P  L  L  M  S  S  C  E  N  U  U  X  V  W  O
U  V  X  U  R  B  C  O  E  S  U  A  S  S  M  P  W  R  Y  L
T  S  R  N  A  N  D  R  O  R  S  E  P  E  R  M  O  O  T  E
F  E  R  A  T  O  S  T  H  E  N  E  S  X  Y  I  S  T  S  M
M  N  O  T  A  S  C  O  M  B  E  S  I  X  C  P  R  U  Y  L
W  I  S  N  R  D  E  X  C  L  V  E  P  O  I  V  S  L  E  N
A  N  N  O  D  A  M  I  N  O  Z  D  F  P  E  A  E  A  S  L
O  N  A  M  P  Y  I  D  L  A  M  I  R  G  C  C  C  F  R  A
A  E  S  O  P  A  B  G  J  L  B  M  A  U  N  S  M  N  C  M
P  P  P  I  C  O  A  E  H  P  R  H  A  M  L  R  M  S  G  A
A  A  A  G  C  N  V  F  R  T  S  C  T  Y  P  V  B  Z  O  P
X  B  E  E  F  E  N  M  O  P  W  R  R  T  Y  C  H  O  O  L
Z  S  I  R  I  Z  E  L  P  T  R  A  L  E  M  E  I  D  W  S
R  I  V  E  B  R  R  E  Y  K  C  O  L  S  O  D  P  F  L  E
T  T  E  H  U  M  B  O  L  D  T  L  R  L  N  S  P  H  I  D
E  S  O  M  E  O  A  F  T  H  A  E  F  E  A  T  A  U  R  E
S  I  N  T  H  I  C  L  A  V  I  U  S  S  D  R  R  A  B  P
U  Z  Z  L  P  E  C  A  E  N  Y  S  O  U  F  I  C  N  D  T
H  E  M  O  R  L  N  N  O  D  A  S  U  S  N  O  H  P  L  A
T  S  O  M  U  C  I  H  F  G  R  O  T  E  H  F  U  U  N  D
A  M  E  E  S  P  T  N  R  Y  A  G  A  A  I  I  S  N  M  O
B  E  F  O  L  R  E  T  I  H  E  S  T  E  B  N  A  M  C  A
S  S  T  A  M  O  O  R  S  U  X  Y  A  C  B  N  L  I  I  C
N  H  D  S  F  R  R  E  A  N  S  T  I  M  M  N  O  L  L  S
```

Answers: page 108

Famous Telescopes. Telescopes at a number of observatories bear the names of donors and scientists, among others. At each of the institutions below, the telescope that is described has a name. These are hidden among the letters on the facing page. Can you find all the names? Can you associate each with the proper telescope? The names you are looking for are given on page 91.

A. Agassiz Station, Harvard	61-inch reflector
B. Allegheny Observatory	30-inch refractor
C. Armagh Observatory	32-inch Schmidt
D. Cambridge University	11¾-inch refractor
E. Catholic University (Santiago)	37-inch reflector
F. Commonwealth Observatory, Canberra	30-inch reflector
G. Dominion Astrophysical Observatory	72-inch reflector
H. Harvard College Observatory	15-inch refractor
I. Kitt Peak National Observatory	158-inch reflector
J. Lick Observatory	36-inch reflector
K. London University Observatory	24-inch reflector
L. Lowell Observatory	13-inch photographic doublet
M. Mount Wilson Observatory	100-inch reflector
N. Palomar Mountain Observatory	200-inch reflector
O. Paris Observatory	13.4-inch astrograph
P. Pulkovo Observatory	9½-inch refractor
Q. Royal Observatory	98-inch reflector
R. Vanderbilt University Observatory	24-inch convertible telescope
S. Warner and Swasey Observatory	24-inch Schmidt
T. Yerkes Observatory	10-inch doublet

A S D F G H T R E D H J K L O P U N B X C B N
C V B D R T Y E D C O B V D E R Y G B C M O L
A H G E M K T P Q W U C V R E T A G H L U R D
A L Z R E M T H E R G R T V B X C M Y S X A K
B U T E S A O M R E A T H J C D W Q P L M N O
F O R Y T Y H E E G D C V W T H I B L P D F W
S O M D N A L R E B M U H T R O N F O R C S T
T H A O T L A M O F S N G T E H O G R A N D E
S T C R I L T E S L O F T E K N S E N M I D A
S U M P L W Q A L A L T H O O U L G H T A H A
T W Q A L V X I Z C P U T T O A I O N R T H D
O B A T G K M R H T E Y W A H T W W M H Y S H
E A S G E V D W I E T E T H E O F A F E R O O
F V W E T I W I D M N K L M R N G V B D C E A
T H I S G C B R U C E R E E T H S Q U I T E B
O R I N G T A F A T E R Y A D W E E B I H T S
L E T S G O O A O N T N O U S U M E L T H I G
S E M X L R S I K D O W N S P K V M D E C U L
W P Z X G I F Y E L S S O R C T E R N J D P T
D U Y I H A W C D B I N Y K M N E P O H D C N
V L T E R Y D S P N K G C L F R Y I C S Q P L
B U K C E T O F K W G T P J T F C E D G H E Q
C B T Y U R I H O E P F G T N C V G E D M N L
Z S Y G J K A E R T Y O L K P B F D E E B H J
P U I R F R G H O M N F P L T Z Z C E D F G H
M K F L V O T P F B N M R S T I P L V C E Q R
K F L A M V F R T E S G J I H T V N M U I O P
W E R O T Y V B M Y T I F G H K L O P T S E C
W D V C B G R T Y U C S D F G N K O P L N M T

Answers: page 109

Mercury (Wednesday)
*Gypsy Planet and
Dream Book*

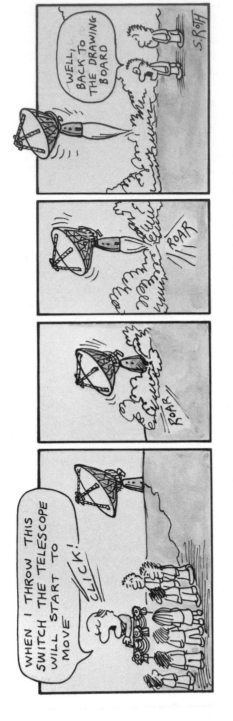

Molecules. During the last few years many molecules have been discovered in space. Below are the chemical formulae for several. Common names are hidden on the next page. First, find the molecules; then identify them with the formulae. The molecules you are seeking are identified on page 92.

A. H_2

B. H_2O

C. H_2S

D. CN

E. CO

F. HCN

G. SiS

H. HDO

I. NH_3

J. H_2CO

K. C_2H

L. CH_3OH

M. CH_3CN

N. CH_3CHO

O. H_2CNH

P. H_2CS

Q. C_2H_5OH

R. $CHOOH$

S. NH_2CHO

Answers: page 110

20th Century Astronomers. The last names of the following contributors to astronomy during the present century will be found in the accompanying search. First, complete all the names; then identify each name with the brief characterization. Hints are on page 92.

1. Henry Norris _____

   A. His detailed studies of open clusters led to definite evidence for absorption of starlight in space.

2. Walter _____

   B. Famous classifier of stellar spectra.

3. Harlow _____

   C. Photographer of the Milky Way.

4. Vesto M. _____

   D. Solar astronomer who established Yerkes Observatory, then Mount Wilson and Palomar.

5. Edwin P. _____

   E. Realized that stars and other objects represented more than one population.

6. Donald H. _____

   F. Discovered radial and rotational velocities of spiral nebulae.

7. Gerard P. _____

   G. Associated with spectrum-luminosity diagram, eclipsing binaries, and much more.

8. Percival _____

   H. Found the recessional velocities of galaxies were proportional to their distance.

9. Otto _____

   I. Solar astronomer who was director of Harvard Observatory.

10. Carl _____

    J. Renowned for studies of planets.

11. Heber D. _____

    K. Contributed to a variety of topics associated with stellar spectroscopy.

12. Annie J. _____

    L. Associated with the discovery of Pluto.

13. Edward E. _____

    M. Galaxies with active nuclei bear his name.

14. George Ellery _____

    N. Found the period-luminosity relation for Cepheid variables.

15. Robert J. _____

    O. Placed the sun far from the center of the Milky Way system.

16. Henrietta S. _____

    P. Debated with *3* on the nature of spiral nebulae.

```
G  V  T  H  S  Q  T  R  A  E  Y  F  G  I  P  K  W  L  M  O
B  A  C  S  D  T  U  R  N  K  L  F  C  K  Q  P  O  A  S  L
L  G  O  O  D  F  E  L  E  L  O  P  T  U  T  U  I  M  N  X
W  H  A  A  O  L  M  H  J  F  E  W  R  I  P  L  L  V  C  S
P  O  L  X  C  R  V  B  T  Y  Y  E  L  P  A  H  S  S  H  A
W  H  E  I  C  E  F  I  R  G  G  E  C  E  W  U  B  J  K  F
C  V  W  K  G  L  U  I  Y  L  V  B  S  R  S  B  D  V  A  K
T  H  E  R  R  P  A  O  L  L  E  O  P  T  A  B  A  A  D  E
L  C  V  R  T  M  E  N  Z  E  L  L  E  W  O  L  S  X  I  P
F  D  O  X  C  U  G  U  E  S  A  E  E  U  F  E  D  P  I  L
A  U  U  R  T  R  O  D  E  S  H  V  E  R  U  I  C  L  M  N
K  E  R  F  T  T  T  U  I  U  U  S  I  T  R  U  C  U  R  C
O  C  V  S  T  Y  I  X  C  R  U  S  T  T  B  A  A  D  D  F
L  E  N  Z  F  M  L  Z  T  E  Q  U  Y  V  T  I  N  J  K  P
B  R  E  H  P  I  L  S  L  I  O  F  E  R  Q  U  N  X  C  V
P  H  E  R  L  I  S  F  G  M  C  E  R  Y  F  B  O  L  L  O
D  A  R  N  A  R  B  B  A  X  X  A  B  B  A  R  N  A  R  D
B  A  R  Y  A  C  E  V  G  T  H  D  N  M  Y  O  P  R  E  E
```

Answers: page 111

Astrocrostics

Start by filling in as many of the definitions as you can. Then transfer the letters to the appropriate locations in the quotation. While these may not lead to a complete word in the latter, enough information may be available to complete the word. These added letters can then be placed in the appropriate location of a definition to give you an added clue as to what that word or words might be. Suppose, for instance, there is a three-letter word in the quotation and you have been able to identify "H" as the middle letter. In many cases the missing letters will be "T" and "E". These then can be transferred to the definitions, and so on.

ASTROCROSTIC I

This is a basic statement attributable to many authors and many books. The clues are in no particular order.

A. Asteroid with largest known orbit

2	21	89	27	23	11	74

B. Not a likely way to describe T. J. J. See

55	8	83	24	98	28

C. Dutch astronomer

49	14	16	31	45	54	85

D. March equinox

51	3	43	19	33	15

E. Procyon is in

20	70	82	12	6	69	40	80	47	91

F. Angle between orbital planes

84	39	13	88	18	97	63	26	95	79	71

G. British radio astronomer

73	96	41	61	9	46

H. Trade name of a filter

44	93	58	48	94	35

I. Nova DQ is another variable star here

81	29	32	92	53	4	38	87	78	62

J. Eighth brightest star in many constellations

59	36	65	1	86

K. Satellite of Saturn   ___ ___ ___ ___ ___ ___
                                                 77   52   34   60   72   25

L. Where the 200-inch can be used .

     ___ ___ ___ ___ ___ ___ ___ ___ ___ ___
     22   17   90   7   37   66   68   75   56   50

M. Passes near Earth   ___ ___ ___ ___
                                        42   67   5   30

N. Optical aberration   ___ ___ ___ ___
                                      57   10   64   76

ASTROCROSTIC I

| 1 J | 2 A | 3 D | • 4 I | 5 M | 6 E | 7 L | 8 B | 9 G | 10 N | 11 A |

| 12 E | 13 F | 14 C | 15 D | • 16 C | 17 L | 18 F | 19 D | 20 E | 21 A | 22 L |

| 23 A | 24 B | • 25 K | 26 F | 27 A | 28 B | 29 I | 30 M | • 31 C | 32 I |

| 33 D | 34 K | • 35 H | 36 J | 37 L | • 38 I | 39 F | 40 E | 41 G | 42 M |

| 43 D | 44 H | 45 C | • 46 G | 47 E | 48 H | 49 C | 50 L | • 51 D | 52 K |

| 53 I | 54 C | • 55 B | 56 L | 57 N | 58 H | • 59 J | 60 K | 61 G | • |

| 62 I | 63 F | 64 N | 65 J | • 66 L | 67 M | 68 L | 69 E | • 70 E | 71 F |

| 72 K | • 73 G | 74 A | 75 L | 76 N | 77 K | 78 I | 79 F | 80 E | • 81 I |

| 82 E | 83 B | • 84 F | 85 C | • 86 J | 87 I | 88 F | • 89 A | 90 L | 91 E |

| 92 I | 93 H | 94 H | 95 F | 96 G | 97 F | 98 B |

Hints: page 92   Answers: page 111

ASTROCROSTIC II

The author or authors have been lost, but where the quotation is from will appear in the first letters of the definitions.

A. Of Samos (Greek spelling)

$\overline{}$ $\overline{88}$ $\overline{186}$ $\overline{169}$ $\overline{25}$ $\overline{60}$ $\overline{199}$ $\overline{156}$ $\overline{128}$ $\overline{119}$ $\overline{78}$ $\overline{100}$

B. Home to William Herschel

$\overline{151}$ $\overline{92}$ $\overline{104}$ $\overline{18}$ $\overline{136}$ $\overline{184}$

C. Rank of Ceres in discovery list of asteroids

$\overline{103}$ $\overline{126}$ $\overline{163}$ $\overline{191}$ $\overline{23}$ $\overline{97}$ $\overline{47}$ $\overline{117}$

D. What you might say to your companion who claims the cold can no longer be endured

$\overline{162}$ $\overline{132}$ $\overline{135}$ $\overline{204}$ $\overline{30}$ $\overline{80}$ $\overline{74}$ $\overline{166}$ $\overline{72}$

$\overline{196}$ $\overline{50}$ $\overline{10}$ $\overline{75}$ $\overline{146}$ $\overline{41}$

E. Messier 97

$\overline{2}$ $\overline{109}$ $\overline{52}$ $\overline{138}$ $\overline{65}$ $\overline{193}$ $\overline{45}$ $\overline{197}$ $\overline{149}$

F. Veil or

$\overline{15}$ $\overline{198}$ $\overline{125}$ $\overline{5}$ $\overline{108}$ $\overline{205}$ $\overline{57}$

G. A mariner's description of Mare Imbrium

$\overline{190}$ $\overline{63}$ $\overline{13}$ $\overline{46}$ $\overline{173}$ $\overline{35}$ $\overline{187}$

H. Component of Jupiter's atmosphere

$\overline{49}$ $\overline{82}$ $\overline{107}$ $\overline{38}$ $\overline{113}$ $\overline{27}$ $\overline{8}$

I. Thought to permeate the universe

$\overline{180}$ $\overline{154}$ $\overline{94}$ $\overline{189}$ $\overline{44}$

J. Lunar companion to Sabine

_____ _____ _____ _____ _____ _____
54   68   174 183 84   9

K. Type of hot star with emission lines in spectrum

_____ _____ _____ _____ _____
77 101 32 3 64

L. Time lapses when radar is used

_____ _____ _____ _____ _____ _____ _____ _____ _____ _____
53 144 17 120 93 24 34 131 102 203

M. Telescope free of coma and spherical aberration

_____ _____ _____ _____ _____ _____ _____ _____ _____ _____ _____ _____
33 178 37 118 160 95 21 1 129 66 176 7

_____ _____ _____
139 112 56

N. Where new moon appears

_____ _____ _____ _____ _____ _____ _____ _____ _____
55 99 195 175 59 143 185 36 76

O. Cataclysmic or

_____ _____ _____ _____ _____ _____ _____ _____
111 98 165 42 87 116 12 62

P. Vacancies in asteroid belt

_____ _____ _____ _____ _____ _____ _____ _____ _____ _____ _____ _____ _____
20 110 83 61 148 105 91 4 141 122 161 145 73

Q. Apparent location of Aldebaran

_____ _____ _____ _____ _____ _____ _____ _____ _____ _____ _____
152 170 182 155 70 81 150 6 200 39 48

R. Species of atomic nuclei

_____ _____ _____ _____ _____ _____ _____ _____
79 86 19 51 134 96 123 14

S. Brightish star in the Sea Snake

$\overline{85}$ $\overline{147}$ $\overline{69}$ $\overline{179}$ $\overline{11}$ $\overline{133}$ $\overline{29}$ $\overline{43}$ $\overline{153}$ $\overline{130}$

T. Physicist son of late, great astronomer (initial last)

$\overline{142}$ $\overline{22}$ $\overline{164}$ $\overline{90}$ $\overline{58}$ $\overline{127}$ $\overline{168}$ $\overline{181}$

U. Molecular state of H where protons have same direction of spin

$\overline{157}$ $\overline{167}$ $\overline{188}$ $\overline{71}$ $\overline{16}$ $\overline{40}$ $\overline{202}$ $\overline{115}$ $\overline{89}$ $\overline{194}$ $\overline{159}$ $\overline{137}$ $\overline{121}$

V. Result of a cloudy night

$\overline{114}$ $\overline{26}$ $\overline{31}$ $\overline{192}$ $\overline{124}$ $\overline{201}$ $\overline{177}$ $\overline{140}$ $\overline{28}$

W. Variable star in the Bull

$\overline{171}$ $\overline{106}$ $\overline{67}$ $\overline{172}$ $\overline{158}$

ASTROCROSTIC II

| 1 M | 2 E | 3 K | 4 P | | 5 F | 6 Q | 7 M | 8 H | 9 J | | 10 D | 11 S |

| 12 O | 13 G | 14 R | | 15 F | 16 U | | 17 L | 18 B | 19 R | 20 P | 21 M |

| 22 T | 23 C | 24 L | 25 A | | 26 V | 27 H | | 28 V | 29 S | 30 D | 31 V | 32 K |

| 33 M | 34 L | 35 G | 36 N | | 37 M | 38 H | 39 Q | | 40 U | 41 D | 42 O |

| 43 S | | 44 I | 45 E | 46 G | 47 C | | 48 Q | 49 H | 50 D | 51 R | 52 E |

| 53 L | 54 J | 55 N | 56 M | 57 F | | 58 T | 59 N | 60 A | | 61 P | 62 O | 63 G |

| 64 K | 65 E | 66 M | | 67 W | 68 J | 69 S | 70 Q | | 71 U | 72 D | 73 P |

| 74 D | 75 D | 76 N | 77 K | | 78 A | 79 R | | 80 D | 81 Q | 82 H | | 83 P |

| 84 J | 85 S | 86 R | 87 O | 88 A | 89 U | | 90 T | 91 P | 92 B | 93 L | 94 I | 95 M |

96 R   97 C   98 O   99 N   100 A   101 K   102 L   103 C   104 B   105 P

106 W   107 H   108 F   109 E   110 P   111 O   112 M   113 H   114 V   115 U

116 O   117 C   118 M   119 A   120 L   121 U   122 P   123 R   124 V   125 F   126 C

127 T   128 A   129 M   130 S   131 L   132 D   133 S   134 R   135 D   136 B

137 U   138 E   139 M   140 V   141 P   142 T   143 N   144 L   145 P   146 D   147 S

148 P   149 E   150 Q   151 B   152 Q   153 S   154 I   155 Q   156 A   157 U   158 W

159 U   160 M   161 P   162 D   163 C   164 T   165 O   166 D   167 U   168 T   169 A

170 Q   171 W   172 W   173 G   174 J   175 N   176 M   177 V   178 M   179 S

180 I   181 T   182 Q   183 J   184 B   185 N   186 A   187 G   188 U   189 I

190 G   191 C   192 V   193 E   194 U   195 N   196 D   197 E   198 F   199 A

200 Q   201 V   202 U   203 L   204 D   205 F   !

Hints: page 92   Answers: page 112

Jupiter (Thursday)
Gypsy Planet and Dream Book

ASTROCROSTIC III

The name of the author of this quotation appears in the downward reading of the first letter of the definitions. The initial letter of the final definition corresponds to the initial letter of the work in which the quotation appears.

A. Where the new moon appears relative to the sun

___ ___ ___ ___ ___ ___
82   103   48   54   33   60

B. Part of shadow defined by penumbra

___ ___ ___ ___ ___ ___ ___
65   92   41   29   75   7   98

C. Meteorite pattern

___ ___ ___ ___ ___ ___ ___ ___ ___ ___ ___ ___ ___
49   91   10   45   66   2   73   52   83   89   14   64   43

D. Hven

___ ___ ___ ___
15   105   96   76

E. "Let me see the chart again, it's

___ ___ ___ ___ ___ ___ ___
25   62   4   40   23   99   81

___ ___ ___ ___ ___ ___ ___ ___
28   94   5   102   13   55   1   90 "

F. Barnard's star is one

___ ___ ___ ___ ___ ___ ___ ___
57   12   37   68   8   97   34   59

G. Realm of astronomy

___ ___ ___ ___ ___ ___ ___ ___ ___ ___
35   87   61   19   47   101   31   38   22   30

H. Pertains to RR Lyrae instability strip

___ ___ ___ ___ ___ ___ ___ ___
63   74   6   56   9   3   26   46

I. Co-author of work on Chinese, Korean, Japanese historical meteor showers

$\overline{\text{24}}$ $\overline{\text{84}}$ $\overline{\text{32}}$ $\overline{\text{71}}$ $\overline{\text{42}}$

J. Zeros

$\overline{\text{67}}$ $\overline{\text{95}}$ $\overline{\text{17}}$ $\overline{\text{27}}$ $\overline{\text{18}}$

K. Either describes a high tide

$\overline{\text{39}}$ $\overline{\text{77}}$ $\overline{\text{104}}$ $\overline{\text{11}}$ $\overline{\text{93}}$ $\overline{\text{69}}$, $\overline{\text{86}}$ $\overline{\text{36}}$ $\overline{\text{51}}$ $\overline{\text{72}}$ $\overline{\text{80}}$

L. Prominent Dutch astronomer

$\overline{\text{53}}$ $\overline{\text{44}}$ $\overline{\text{21}}$ $\overline{\text{78}}$

M. Pertaining to intersection of planet's orbit with ecliptic

$\overline{\text{88}}$ $\overline{\text{70}}$ $\overline{\text{100}}$ $\overline{\text{20}}$ $\overline{\text{16}}$

N. Hydroxyl radical, oxygen molecule

$\overline{\text{58}}$ $\overline{\text{50}}$, $\overline{\text{85}}$ $\overline{\text{79}}$

ASTROCROSTIC III

```
___  ___  ___   •  ___  ___  ___  ___   •  ___  ___   •  ___
1 E  2 C  3 H      4 E  5 E  6 H  7 B      8 F  9 H      10 C

___  ___   •  ___  ___  ___  ___  ___   •  ___  ___  ___  ___
11 K 12 F     13 E 14 C 15 D 16 M 17 J     18 J 19 G 20 M 21 L

___  ___  ___  ___  ___   •  ___  ___  ___  ___   •  ___  ___  ___
22 G 23 E 24 I 25 E 26 H     27 J 28 E 29 B 30 G     31 G 32 I

___  ___   •  ___  ___  ___   •  ___  ___  ___  ___  ___   •  ___  ___
33 A 34 F     35 G 36 K 37 F     38 G 39 K 40 E 41 B 42 I     43 C

___  ___  ___  ___  ___   •  ___  ___  ___   •  ___  ___  ___  ___
44 L 45 C 46 H 47 G 48 A     49 C 50 N 51 K     52 C 53 L 54 A

___  ___  ___   •  ___  ___  ___   •  ___  ___  ___   •  ___  ___
55 E 56 H 57 F     58 N 59 F 60 A     61 G 62 E     63 H 64 C

___   •  ___  ___  ___   •  ___  ___   •  ___  ___  ___   •  ___  ___
65 B     66 C 67 J 68 F     69 K 70 M     71 I 72 K     73 C 74 H

___  ___  ___   •  ___  ___  ___   •  ___  ___  ___  ___  ___   •
75 B 76 D 77 K     78 L 79 N     80 K 81 E 82 A 83 C 84 I

___  ___   •  ___  ___  ___  ___  ___  ___  ___  ___  ___  ___
85 N 86 K     87 G 88 M 89 C 90 E 91 C 92 B 93 K 94 E 95 J

___  ___  ___  ___  ___   •  ___  ___  ___  ___  ___  ___
96 D 97 F 98 B 99 E 100 M    101 G 102 E 103 A 104 K 105 D
```

Hints: page 93   Answers: page 112

ASTROCROSTIC IV

The quotation is a loose translation that might have been taken from the work of a great astronomer. When read down, the first letters of the definitions will spell out his name and a translated version of the work's title.

A. Home to Tobias Mayer ____ ____ ____ ____ ____ ____ ____ ____ ____
205 98 91 36 95 111 153 57 177

B. Planetary tables of 1252

____ ____ ____ ____ ____ ____ ____ ____ ____
17 214 207 69 204 108 227 140 210

C. Nodes or apsides

____ ____ ____ ____ ____ ____
89 53 201 20 219 166

D. Venus

____ ____ ____ ____ ____ ____
151 31 97 120 9 70

E. Gravitation is an example of one

____ ____ ____ ____ ____ ____ ____ ____ ____ ____ ____ ____
106 110 81 206 186 113 2 90 230 138 134 159

F. Site of Dearborn Observatory

____ ____ ____ ____ ____ ____ ____ ____
39 162 93 185 145 77 33 173

G. Part of solar atmosphere

____ ____ ____ ____ ____ ____ ____ ____ ____ ____ ____
212 168 74 109 42 49 82 222 188 202 172

H. Causes apples to fall ____ ____ ____ ____ ____ ____ ____
165 181 136 43 117 65 196

I. Astronomers' source of support? ____ ____ ____ ____
86 171 16 64

J. Discoverer of Thetis

<u>   </u> <u>   </u> <u>   </u> <u> </u> <u> </u> <u>   </u>
116 216 122 92 7 161

K. Where sun is during late April

<u> </u> <u> </u> <u>   </u> <u> </u> <u> </u> <u>   </u> <u> </u> <u> </u>
24 11 175 78 88 195 72 34

L. Where the new moon appears

100 46 22 203 76 190 14 194 224 229 182 226

M. Effect observed in sunspots

192 193 29 169 137 123 180 58

N. Identified "nebulium" lines

75 12 47 220 125 149 51

O. Useful piece of equipment

118 170 178 25 59 4 107 176 135 63 68 41

P. Path of one particle relative to another

208 131 160 50 187 158 103 45

Q. To the list of asteroids, Temple

154 101 54 3 112 84 128 141 218 26 139

R. Of the brightest stars, Antares is the

21 183 38 143 198 27 130

S. Least squares is an example of a

228 184 13 119 133 215

T. Basis of eclipsing binary light elements

___ ___ ___ ___ ___
61 217 37 105 23

___ ___ ___ ___ ___ ___ ___ ___ ___
147 142 8 200 73 144 30 221 87

U. Sunspot

___ ___ ___ ___ ___ ___ ___
96 18 121 83 67 126 152

___ ___ ___ ___ ___ ___ ___
1 60 35 80 114 155

V. Of the bright stars, Miaplacidus is the

___ ___ ___ ___ ___ ___ ___ ___ ___ ___ ___ ___
52 223 99 71 209 15 213 164 62 157 40 19

W. Reaction that occurs with the absorption of heat

___ ___ ___ ___ ___ ___ ___ ___ ___ ___ ___
132 225 102 167 94 191 28 56 189 10 146

X. Frequency with which a star is seen between moon's cusps

___ ___ ___ ___ ___
85 5 148 174 127

Y. Reseau

___ ___ ___ ___
199 150 79 129

Z. When the sea is out

___ ___ ___ ___ ___ ___ ___
44 115 197 32 66 156 48

AA. "Books and the Sky"

___ ___ ___ ___ ___ ___ ___
6 124 179 163 55 211 104

Uma (The Horse)
Japanese Zodiac
from *Family Crests*

| 1 U | 2 E | 3 Q | 4 O | 5 X | | 6 AA | 7 J | 8 T | 9 D | 10 W | 11 K |

| 12 N | 13 S | 14 L | 15 V | 16 I | 17 B | 18 U | 19 V | 20 C | 21 R |

| 22 L | 23 T | 24 K | 25 O | 26 Q | 27 R | 28 W | 29 M | 30 T | 31 D | 32 Z |

| 33 F | 34 K | 35 U | 36 A | 37 T | 38 R | 39 F | 40 V | 41 O | 42 G |

| 43 H | 44 Z | 45 P | 46 L | 47 N | 48 Z | 49 G | 50 P | 51 N | 52 V |

| 53 C | 54 Q | 55 AA | 56 W | 57 A | 58 M | 59 O | 60 U | 61 T | 62 V | 63 O |

| 64 I | 65 H | 66 Z | 67 U | 68 O | 69 B | 70 D | 71 V | 72 K | 73 T | 74 G |

| 75 N | 76 L | 77 F | 78 K | 79 Y | 80 U | 81 E | 82 G | 83 U | 84 Q |

| 85 X | 86 I | 87 T | 88 K | 89 C | 90 E | 91 A | 92 J | 93 F | 94 W | 95 A |

| 96 U | 97 D | 98 A | 99 V | 100 L | 101 Q | 102 W | 103 P | 104 AA | 105 T | 106 E |

| 107 O | 108 B | 109 G | 110 E | 111 A | 112 Q | 113 E | 114 U | 115 Z | 116 J | 117 H |

| 118 O | 119 S | 120 D | 121 U | 122 J | 123 M | 124 AA | 125 N | 126 U | 127 X |

| 128 Q | 129 Y | 130 R | 131 P | 132 W | 133 S | 134 E | 135 O | 136 H | 137 M | 138 E |

| 139 Q | 140 B | 141 Q | 142 T | 143 R | 144 T | 145 F | 146 W | 147 T | 148 X | 149 N |

| 150 Y | 151 D | 152 U | 153 A | 154 Q | 155 U | 156 Z | 157 V | 158 P | 159 E | 160 P |

| 161 J | 162 F | 163 AA | 164 V | 165 H | 166 C | 167 W | 168 G | 169 M | 170 O | 171 I |

| 172 G | 173 F | 174 X | 175 K | 176 O | 177 A | 178 O | 179 AA | 180 M | 181 H | 182 L |

| 183 R | 184 S | 185 F | 186 E | 187 P | 188 G | 189 W | 190 L | 191 W | 192 M |

$\overline{193\ M}$ $\overline{194\ L}$ $\overset{\bullet}{\overline{195\ K}}$ $\overline{196\ H}$ $\overline{197\ Z}$ $\overline{198\ R}$ $\overline{199\ Y}$ $\overline{200\ T}$ $\overline{201\ C}$ $\overline{202\ G}$ $\overline{203\ L}$

$\overline{204\ B}$ $\overline{205\ A}$ $\overset{\bullet}{\overline{206\ E}}$ $\overline{207\ B}$ $\overline{208\ P}$ $\overline{209\ V}$ $\overline{210\ B}$ $\overset{\bullet}{\overline{211\ AA}}$ $\overline{212\ G}$ $\overline{213\ V}$

$\overline{214\ B}$ $\overline{215\ S}$ $\overset{\bullet}{\overline{216\ J}}$ $\overline{217\ T}$ $\overset{\bullet}{\overline{218\ Q}}$ $\overline{219\ C}$ $\overset{\bullet}{\overline{220\ N}}$ $\overline{221\ T}$ $\overline{222\ G}$ $\overset{\bullet}{\overline{223\ V}}$

$\overline{224\ L}$ $\overset{\bullet}{\overline{225\ W}}$ $\overline{226\ L}$ $\overline{227\ B}$ $\overline{228\ S}$ $\overline{229\ L}$ $\overline{230\ E}$

Hints: page 93   Answers: page 113

ASTROCROSTIC V

The quotation is a loose translation that might have been taken from the principal work of a truly great scientist. The first letters of the definitions will spell out his name and the work.

A. Between stars

$\overline{124}$ $\overline{14}$ $\overline{60}$ $\overline{135}$ $\overline{76}$ $\overline{91}$ $\overline{38}$ $\overline{147}$ $\overline{57}$ $\overline{41}$ $\overline{154}$ $\overline{100}$

$\overline{77}$ $\overline{127}$ $\overline{109}$ $\overline{120}$ $\overline{74}$ $\overline{47}$

B. For planetary studies

$\overline{149}$ $\overline{118}$ $\overline{71}$ $\overline{157}$ $\overline{106}$ $\overline{115}$ $\overline{55}$ $\overline{123}$ $\overline{140}$ $\overline{153}$

C. A pseudoscience

$\overline{29}$ $\overline{80}$ $\overline{69}$ $\overline{148}$ $\overline{13}$ $\overline{93}$ $\overline{108}$ $\overline{152}$ $\overline{94}$

D. Describes binary

$\overline{83}$ $\overline{46}$ $\overline{105}$ $\overline{39}$ $\overline{116}$

E. Star in Gemini

$\overline{143}$ $\overline{10}$ $\overline{45}$ $\overline{126}$ $\overline{34}$ $\overline{64}$

F. Home to Old Eli astronomy department

$\overline{145}$ $\overline{130}$ $\overline{134}$ $\overline{121}$ $\overline{36}$ $\overline{155}$ $\overline{3}$ $\overline{104}$

G. "Point" in spacetime

$\overline{92}$ $\overline{7}$ $\overline{27}$ $\overline{128}$ $\overline{72}$

H. Stage in stellar evolution

$\overline{25}$ $\overline{110}$ $\overline{102}$ $\overline{133}$ $\overline{144}$ $\overline{85}$ $\overline{33}$ $\overline{56}$ $\overline{96}$ $\overline{119}$

I. Milky Way feature ___ ___ ___ ___ ___ ___ ___ ___ ___
107 73 117   51   12 151 101   53   28

___ ___ ___ ___ ___ ___
40 158   4   87   67   79

J. A Struve ___ ___ ___ ___
48 138   11 150

K. Used for comparison spectrum

___ ___ ___ ___ ___ ___ ___ ___
84   21 103 137   58 114   22   89

L. Space vehicle ___ ___ ___ ___ ___
49 142   18 131   62

M. Identified with Hubble ___ ___ ___ ___ ___ ___ ___ ___
5   42   66 112   61   75   17   24

N. Alternative nucleus ___ ___ ___ ___ ___ ___ ___
86   43   97 146   59   35 122

O. New stars ___ ___ ___ ___ ___
30   54   88   6   81

P. Observing aid ___ ___ ___ ___ ___
129 139   15   90   1

Q. Comet model (my spelling) ___ ___ ___ ___
8   68   23   31

R. Sketcher of telescopes ___ ___ ___ ___ ___ ___
98   65   37   9 132   19

S. Line of equal light intensity ___ ___ ___ ___ ___ ___ ___ ___
44 125   99   63   2   70   52   26

T. Southern variable star

___ ___ ___ ___ ___ ___ ___ ___ ___ ___ ___ ___
78 113   32 111   16 136   82   20   50   95 156 141

ASTROCROSTIC V

```
 1 P   2 S   3 F      • 4 I   5 M   6 O   7 G   8 Q   9 R   10 E  11 J

12 I  13 C  14 A  15 P  16 T     • 17 M  18 L  19 R  20 T  21 K      •

22 K  23 Q  24 M  25 H  26 S  27 G  28 I   • 29 C  30 O  31 Q         •

32 T  33 H  34 E     • 35 N  36 F  37 R  38 A  39 D  40 I  41 A  42 M

43 N    • 44 S  45 E    • 46 D  47 A  48 J  49 L  50 T  51 I  52 S

53 I  54 O  55 B  56 H  57 A    • 58 K  59 N    • 60 A  61 M  62 L    •

63 S  64 E  65 R  66 M  67 I  68 Q  69 C    • 70 S  71 B    • 72 G

73 I  74 A  75 M  76 A    • 77 A  78 T  79 I  80 C  81 O  82 T       •

83 D  84 K  85 H    • 86 N  87 I  88 O  89 K  90 P  91 A  92 G

93 C  94 C    • 95 T  96 H  97 N  98 R  99 S  100 A  101 I  102 H  103 K

104 F  105 D  106 B    • 107 I  108 C    • 109 A  110 H  111 T    • 112 M  113 T

114 K  115 B  116 D  117 I    • 118 B  119 H    • 120 A  121 F  122 N    •

123 B  124 A  125 S  126 E  127 A  128 G  129 P  130 F    • 131 L  132 R

133 H  134 F  135 A  136 T  137 K    • 138 J  139 P  140 B  141 T  142 L    • 143 E

144 H  145 F  146 N  147 A  148 C  149 B    • 150 J  151 I    • 152 C  153 B

154 A  155 F  156 T  157 B  158 I
```

Hints: page 93   Answers: page 113

The quotation is from a classic work of recent times. First letters of the definitions spell out the name of the author and title of the book.

A. Time-keeping system based strictly on the sun's motion

—— —— —— —— —— —— —— —— —— —— —— —— —— ——
190 265 85 276 175 15 255 124 240 104 153 189 251 51

B. Apparent magnitude of a star at 10 parsecs with no absorption

—— —— —— —— —— —— —— ——
90 12 245 264 170 78 195 215

—— —— —— —— —— —— —— —— ——
236 289 144 110 71 258 62 7 204

C. Name for our galaxy

—— —— —— —— —— —— —— ——
214 285 38 105 127 246 272 136

D. Abbreviation for type of time

—— —— —— ——
83 230 163 186

E. Pattern of oscillations where nodes remain fixed in position

—— —— —— —— —— —— —— —— —— —— —— ——
68 181 6 109 88 241 219 116 57 256 46 121

F. At an early time he was concerned with vanished civilizations

—— —— —— —— —— —— —— —— —— ——
35 278 166 234 157 44 224 23 74 213

G. His name is associated with laws of motion

—— —— —— —— —— —— —— —— —— —— —— —— —— ——
25 202 96 41 232 217 171 56 148 182 131 274 141 277

H. British astrophysicist (initials last)

—— —— —— —— —— —— —— —— —— —— ——
47 275 100 198 11 79 280 193 158 227 93

I. Measure of reflectivity

                                       ___ ___ ___ ___ ___ ___

                                     231 52 122 164 152 13

J. Recent bright object   ___ ___ ___ ___ ___ ___ ___ ___ ___

                       115 16 54 150 290 192 159 91 165

K. Early observer of galaxy spectra   ___ ___ ___ ___ ___ ___ ___

                         34 169 180 288 60 259 67

L. Discoverer of Pluto minus the degree in business administration

                                   ___ ___ ___ ___ ___

                                   112 36 125 73 145

M. Descriptive terms for temperature and color of very early-type stars

                               ___ ___ ___ ___ ___ ___ ___ ___

                       5 86 229 108 82 28 134 261

N. Passive U.S. satellite   ___ ___ ___ ___

                              184 172 75 233

O. Anathema for an eclipse observer

                         ___ ___ ___ ___ ___ ___ ___ ___ ___

                 287 26 267 48 10 129 138 77 242

P. Searcher for trans-Neptunian planet   ___ ___ ___ ___

                             59 282 130 39

Q. Venusian analog to air glow

               ___ ___ ___ ___ ___ ___ ___ ___ ___ ___

          102 228 208 133 188 176 114 200 243 63

R. Variable star in the Crow   ___ ___ ___ ___ ___ ___ ___

                 76 139 249 111 210 65 281

S. Hemisphere from which the star in R is visible

                   ___ ___ ___ ___ ___ ___ ___ ___

              254 132 87 146 101 30 196 151

T. Asteroids number 85, 92, and 98, discovered by Peters

___	___	,	___	___	___	___	___	___	,	___	___	___
206	221		37	266	92	218	142	237		128	271	203

___	___	___	___	___	___
270	187	283	162	250	9

U. Position of sun relative to equator, seen from U.S.A. during summer

___	___	___	___	___	___	___
72	49	135	173	113	107	2

V. Brought fame to Einstein

___	___	___	___	___	___	___	___	___	___	___
167	247	209	244	40	123	154	24	149	137	194

___	___	___	___	___	___	___	___	___	___
263	33	99	235	257	58	103	45	223	197

W. Early believer that asteroids never formed a single body

___	___	___	___
156	174	29	212

X. Mathematician of Cnidus

___	___	___	___	___	___	___
4	98	262	160	178	50	95

Y. Collision between a photon and an energetic electron that transfers some of the latter's energy to the former

___	___	___	___	___	___	___
1	20	226	70	252	269	291

___	___	___	___	___	___	___
279	97	183	207	119	191	17

___	___	___	___	___	___
43	222	118	55	205	155

Z. About one minute of arc for the human eye

___	___	___	___	___	___	___	___	___
14	66	147	94	273	18	248	199	220

___	___	___	___	___
27	61	3	168	260

AA. 105 in the days the item in *A* was used

84	42

BB. Spectral types referred to in *M*

238	8

CC. Abbreviation for a type of time

21	201

DD. Sixth satellite of Saturn

31	120	64	216

EE. The author's preferred spelling of past participle of verb meaning to indicate

22	140	177	32	286

FF. Displacement of spectral lines due to gravitational redshift

253	53	106	284	126	69	143	185

19	161	239	225	179	81

GG. Not north

89	117	268	211	80

1 Y	2 U	3 Z	4 X	5 M	6 E	7 B	8 BB	9 T	10 O
11 H	12 B	13 I	14 Z	15 A	16 J	17 Y	18 Z	19 FF	20 Y
21 CC	22 EE	23 F	24 V	25 G	26 O	27 Z	28 M	29 W	30 S
31 DD	32 EE	33 V	34 K	35 F	36 L	37 T	38 C	39 P	40 V
41 G	42 AA	43 Y	44 F	45 V	46 E	47 H	48 O	49 U	50 X
51 A	52 I	53 FF	54 J	55 Y	56 G	57 E	58 V	59 P	60 K
61 Z	62 B	63 Q	64 DD	65 R	66 Z	67 K	68 E	69 FF	70 Y
71 B	72 U	73 L	74 F	75 N	76 R	77 O	78 B	79 H	80 GG
81 FF	82 M	83 D	84 AA	85 A	86 M	87 S	88 E	89 GG	90 B
91 J	92 T	93 H	94 Z	95 X	96 G	97 Y	98 X	99 V	100 H
101 S	102 Q	103 V	104 A	105 C	106 FF	107 U	108 M	109 E	110 B
111 R	112 L	113 U	114 Q	115 J	116 E	117 GG	118 Y	119 Y	120 DD
121 E	122 I	123 V	124 A	125 L	126 FF	127 C	128 T	129 O	130 P
131 G	132 S	133 Q	134 M	135 U	136 C	137 V	138 O	139 R	140 EE
141 G	142 T	143 FF	144 B	145 L	146 S	147 Z	148 G	149 V	150 J
151 S	152 I	153 A	154 V	155 Y	156 W	157 F	158 H	159 J	160 X
161 FF	162 T	163 D	164 I	165 J	166 F	167 V	168 Z	169 K	170 B
171 G	172 N	173 U	174 W	175 A	176 Q	177 EE	178 X	179 FF	180 K	181 E

———— · —————— · ——— ————
182 *G* 183 *Y* 184 *N* 185 *FF* 186 *D*　187 *T* 188 *Q* 189 *A*　190 *A* 191 *Y*

　 · ——— · ——— ——— —— · ————
192 *J*　193 *H* 194 *V*　195 *B* 196 *S* 197 *V* 198 *H* 199 *Z* 200 *Q*　201 *CC*

—— · ——— ——— ——— ——— ——— ——— —— · ——
202 *G*　203 *T* 204 *B* 205 *Y* 206 *T* 207 *Y* 208 *Q* 209 *V* 210 *R*　211 *GG*

—— · ——— ——— ——— ——— —— · ———
212 *W* 213 *F*　214 *C* 215 *B* 216 *DD* 217 *G* 218 *T* 219 *E* 220 *Z*　221 *T*

—— · ——— ——— —— · ——— ——— ——— · —— ——
222 *Y*　223 *V* 224 *F* 225 *FF*　226 *Y* 227 *H* 228 *Q* 229 *M*　230 *D* 231 *I*

—— ——— ——— ——— —— · ——— · —— ——
232 *G* 233 *N* 234 *F* 235 *V* 236 *B* 237 *T*　238 *BB* 239 *FF*　240 *A* 241 *E*

—— ——— ——— · ——— ——— ——— ——— —— · ——
242 *O* 243 *Q* 244 *V* 245 *B*　246 *C* 247 *V* 248 *Z* 249 *R* 250 *T*　251 *A*

—— —— · ——— ——— ——— ——— ——— ——— ——— ——— ——
252 *Y* 253 *FF*　254 *S* 255 *A* 256 *E* 257 *V* 258 *B* 259 *K* 260 *Z* 261 *M* 262 *X*

· —— ——— ——— ——— —— · ——— · —— —— · ——
263 *V* 264 *B* 265 *A* 266 *T* 267 *O*　268 *GG* 269 *Y*　270 *T* 271 *T*　272 *C*

—— · ——— ——— ——— ——— ——— ——— ——— ——— ——— ———
273 *Z* 274 *G*　275 *H* 276 *A* 277 *G* 278 *F* 279 *Y* 280 *H* 281 *R* 282 *P* 283 *T*

—— · ——— · —— ——— ——— ——— ——
284 *FF*　285 *C* 286 *EE*　287 *O* 288 *K* 289 *B* 290 *J* 291 *Y*

Hints: page 94 　　　　　　　　　　　　　 Answers: page 114

ASTROCROSTIC VII

The quotation is from an American poet. His name and the title will appear in the first letters of the definitions.

A. Sirius B is one

—— —— —— —— —— —— —— —— —— ——
85 135 251 185 32 343 217 307 153 286

B. Apparent home of M 31

—— —— —— —— —— —— —— —— ——
224 262 122 76 327 111 293 182 362

C. 0.307 parsec

—— —— —— —— —— —— —— —— ——
268 346 149 44 298 289 128 195 370

D. Sun's apparent path

—— —— —— —— —— —— —— —— —— —— ——
364 215 7 166 96 175 336 193 242 296 206

E. Location of U. S. Naval Observatory's Arizona site

—— —— —— —— —— ——
183 56 21 304 341 325

—— —— —— —— —— —— —— —— ——
287 67 231 273 367 34 115 295 46

F. Familiar lines of the twentieth element and abbreviation for eleventh

—— —— —— —— —— —— ——
139 107 163 266 253 33 322

G. Long-wavelength spectral region

—— —— —— —— —— —— —— ——
142 200 351 132 16 321 82 281

H. The name of Kepler's relation between orbital period and distance

—— —— —— —— —— —— —— —— —— ——
333 190 157 100 12 356 350 246 274 180

—— —— —— —— —— —— —— —— —— —— ——
317 102 258 290 162 248 277 226 204 239 30

I. Found in Saturn's atmosphere

‾‾ ‾‾ ‾‾ ‾‾ ‾‾ ‾‾ ‾‾
187 61 93 150 279 4 300

J. Variable star in the Fly

‾‾ ‾‾ ‾‾ ‾‾ ‾‾
20 232 301 49 88

K. Adams' planet

‾‾ ‾‾ ‾‾ ‾‾ ‾‾ ‾‾ ‾‾
18 241 192 313 344 25 73

L. Maybe the greatest observer

‾‾ ‾‾ ‾‾ ‾‾ ‾‾ ‾‾ ‾‾ ‾‾ ‾‾
1 97 358 167 250 65 202 79 256

M. Famous Harvard publication

‾‾ ‾‾ ‾‾
173 118 306

N. Cause of "the old moon in the new moon's arms"

‾‾ ‾‾ ‾‾ ‾‾ ‾‾ ‾‾ ‾‾ ‾‾ ‾‾ ‾‾
366 319 17 178 89 257 330 60 169 207

O. Extracted organic matter from the Orgueil meteorite (initial last)

‾‾ ‾‾ ‾‾ ‾‾ ‾‾
272 86 48 291 72

P. Which was the first asteroid discovered by Hind?

‾‾ ‾‾ ‾‾ ‾‾ ‾‾ ‾‾ ‾‾ ‾‾ ‾‾
121 354 53 158 303 259 209 84 218

Q. Contemporary of Homer who wrote on astronomical matters

‾‾ ‾‾ ‾‾ ‾‾ ‾‾ ‾‾
6 133 71 271 310 324

R. Computed positions for an object over a period of time

‾‾ ‾‾ ‾‾ ‾‾ ‾‾ ‾‾ ‾‾ ‾‾ ‾‾
234 37 31 136 214 282 326 144 130

S. Conservation of it causes a contracting body to spin more rapidly

$$\overline{\rule{1em}{0pt}} \ \overline{\rule{1em}{0pt}} \ \overline{\rule{1em}{0pt}} \ \overline{\rule{1em}{0pt}} \ \overline{\rule{1em}{0pt}} \ \overline{\rule{1em}{0pt}} \ \overline{\rule{1em}{0pt}}$$
264 229 316 275 294 110 244

240 212 27 54 70 368 179 78

T. The range of wavelengths from millimeters to meters within which the Earth's atmosphere is transparent to radiation

57 129 249 269 40 138 235 223 10 340 80

U. Point in a planet's orbit where it passes from north of the ecliptic to south

117 332 52 353 151 221 270 147 92 108

265 164 19 205

V. Bode's oft forgotten companion

146 311 335 261 68 112

W. Type of diagram that shows the frequencies with which stars appear at various locations in the spectrum-luminosity diagram

156 210 355 87

X. Zero for a circle, one for a parabola

245 238 189 338 64 134 38 255 177 47 201 302

Y. Orbital quantum number associated with the answer to S

14 59 188 127 236 198 283

Z. Small irregularities in the moon's motion due to the sun and planets

13 120 45 225 363 184 219 280

AA. Any mathematical representation of the universe

191	91	285	29	357	104	309	75	284	36	233

BB. Lunar crater, 42 miles in diameter, at the head of a valley 115 miles long

9	35	361	199	160	98

CC. When no northern lights have been observed, it is likely that previously there was

141	227	41	308	58	171	77

24	323	276	94	51	292	196	125

DD. A satellite of Mars

62	174	315	328	26	143

EE. Measure of intrinsic brightness

152	288	159	220	339	222	318	123

331	369	267	359	5	22	208	105	95

FF. Season during which the full moon is lowest in the sky

101	228	165	337	3	211

GG. Position of Ceres in a listing of asteroids by discovery dates

113	365	28	74	320	109	197	230

HH. Used to measure extinction

50	352	116	154	170	83	63	297	263

II.   Same as *T* but for visual light _____ _____ _____ _____ _____ _____ _____

                                              66   348 329 243 252 124 194

                                        278 305 103 126 114 168

JJ.   Why this book won't sell _____ _____ _____ _____ _____ _____ _____ _____

                       314 213 69   8   23 342 172 145

KK. Discovered uranium fission

                       216 43 254 90 186 247 2 347

LL.   Famous catalogue

                       137 203 42 260 119 15 99

MM. Region about a star where life might exist

                     176 360 39 312 345 299 140 55 181

NN. Early Amercian observer of Venus

                161 106 11 155 237 148 81 334 131 371 349

ASTROCROSTIC VII

1 L	2 KK	3 FF	4 I	• 5 EE	• 6 Q	7 D	8 JJ	9 BB	10 T	•
11 NN	12 H	13 Z	• 14 Y	15 LL	16 G	17 N	18 K	19 U	• 20 J	
21 E	22 EE	23 JJ	24 CC	25 K	26 DD	27 S	28 GG	29 AA	• 30 H	31 R
32 A	33 F	• 34 E	35 BB	36 AA	• 37 R	38 X	39 MM	40 T	41 CC	
42 LL	• 43 KK	44 C	45 Z	• 46 E	47 X	48 O	49 J	50 HH	51 CC	
52 U	• 53 P	54 S	55 MM	56 E	• 57 T	58 CC	59 Y	60 N	61 I	

62 DD 63 HH 64 X   65 L 66 II 67 E 68 V 69 JJ 70 S 71 Q

72 O 73 K 74 GG 75 AA 76 B 77 CC 78 S 79 L   80 T 81 NN

82 G 83 HH 84 P   85 A 86 O 87 W   88 J 89 N 90 KK 91 AA

92 U 93 I 94 CC 95 EE   96 D 97 L 98 BB 99 LL 100 H 101 FF

102 H 103 II 104 AA   105 EE 106 NN 107 F 108 U 109 GG 110 S 111 B 112 V

113 GG 114 II   115 E 116 HH 117 U   118 M 119 LL 120 Z 121 P 122 B

123 EE   124 II 125 CC 126 II   127 Y 128 C 129 T 130 R 131 NN 132 G

133 Q   134 X 135 A 136 R 137 LL   138 T 139 F 140 MM 141 CC   142 G

143 DD 144 R 145 JJ 146 V 147 U 148 NN 149 C   150 I 151 U 152 EE 153 A

154 HH   155 NN 156 W 157 H   158 P 159 EE 160 BB 161 NN 162 H 163 F

164 U 165 FF 166 D 167 L   168 II 169 N 170 HH 171 CC 172 JJ   173 M

174 DD   175 D 176 MM 177 X 178 N 179 S 180 H 181 MM 182 B   183 E

184 Z 185 A 186 KK   187 I 188 Y 189 X 190 H   191 AA 192 K 193 D

194 II 195 C 196 CC 197 GG 198 Y   199 BB 200 G   201 X 202 L 203 LL

204 H 205 U 206 D 207 N 208 EE 209 P 210 W   211 FF 212 S 213 JJ

214 R   215 D 216 KK 217 A   218 P 219 Z 220 EE 221 U   222 EE 223 T

224 B 225 Z 226 H 227 CC 228 FF 229 S   230 GG 231 E   232 J 233 AA 234 R

235 T   236 Y 237 NN 238 X 239 H 240 S 241 K   242 D 243 II 244 S

245 X 246 H   247 KK 248 H 249 T   250 L 251 A 252 II 253 F   254 KK

— 87 —

_____ _____ _____ •_____ _____ _____ _____ _____ _____ •_____
255 X 256 L 257 N 258 H 259 P 260 LL 261 V 262 B 263 HH 264 S

_____ _____ •_____ _____ _____ _____ _____ _____ _____ •_____
265 U 266 F 267 EE 268 C 269 T 270 U 271 Q 272 O 273 E 274 H

_____ _____ •_____ •_____ _____ _____ _____ _____ _____ _____•
275 S 276 CC 277 H 278 II 279 I 280 Z 281 G 282 R 283 Y 284 AA

_____ _____ _____ •_____ _____ •_____ _____ _____ _____ _____
285 AA 286 A 287 E 288 EE 289 C 290 H 291 O 292 CC 293 B 294 S

_____ •_____ _____ _____ _____ _____ •_____ _____ _____ _____
295 E 296 D 297 HH 298 C 299 MM 300 I 301 J 302 X 303 P 304 E

_____ _____ _____ _____ •_____ _____ _____ _____ _____ •_____
305 II 306 M 307 A 308 CC 309 AA 310 Q 311 V 312 MM 313 K 314 JJ

_____ _____ _____ _____ •_____ _____ _____ •_____ _____ _____•
315 DD 316 S 317 H 318 EE 319 N 320 GG 321 G 322 F 323 CC 324 Q

_____ _____ _____ •_____ _____ _____ _____ •_____ _____ _____•
325 E 326 R 327 B 328 DD 329 II 330 N 331 EE 332 U 333 H 334 NN

_____ _____ _____ _____ •_____ _____ _____ _____ _____ •_____•
335 V 336 D 337 FF 338 X 339 EE 340 T 341 E 342 JJ 343 A 344 K

_____ •_____ _____ •_____ _____ _____ _____ _____ _____ _____•
345 MM 346 C 347 KK 348 II 349 NN 350 H 351 G 352 HH 353 U 354 P

_____ _____ _____ _____ _____ _____ •_____ _____ •_____ _____
355 W 356 H 357 AA 358 L 359 EE 360 MM 361 BB 362 B 363 Z 364 D

_____ _____ •_____ _____ _____ _____ _____
365 GG 366 N 367 E 368 S 369 EE 370 C 371 MM

Hints: page 95   Answers: page 115

Venus (Friday)
*Gypsy Planet and
Dream Book*

Hints

On the following pages are some additional clues to help you with various puzzles before you have to turn to the answers.

Astrobits: Cryptograms

The planet's name is indicated:

1. First word
2. First word
3. First word
4. First word
5. Last word
6. Last word
7. Last word
8. Fifth word

Astrobits: Who Observes Which Planet?

To help you identify the observers and their planets, the following table may be useful. For each clue, place an X in the appropriate location when you are certain that that person does not observe the given planet. For example, since no person observes the planet named for him or her, X's have already been entered in the table. When you have identified the observer of a planet, place an O in the proper location and X's in all the other locations in that row and in that column.

	Mercury	Venus	Mars	Jupiter	Saturn	Uranus	Neptune	Pluto
Mr. Mercury	X	___	___	___	___	___	___	___
Ms. Venus	___	X	___	___	___	___	___	___
Mr. Mars	___	___	X	___	___	___	___	___
Mr. Jupiter	___	___	___	X	___	___	___	___
Mr. Saturn	___	___	___	___	X	___	___	___
Mr. Uranus	___	___	___	___	___	X	___	___
Mr. Neptune	___	___	___	___	___	___	X	___
Mr. Pluto	___	___	___	___	___	___	___	X

Astrobits: Telescope Allocations

In order to help you allocate the telescopes, the following table is provided. When filled out correctly, the answers will be obvious.

	1st Dome	2nd Dome	3rd Dome	4th Dome	5th Dome
Telescope					
State					
Tobacco					
Drink					
Wildlife					

Astrobits: Atomic Composition of Constellations

Splitting up the names in the following way will help.

7. $C + IR + C + I + N + U + S$
8. $LI + B + RA$
9. $MO + N + O + C + ER + OS$
10. $O + C + TA + N + S$
11. $P + I + S + CE + S$
12. $P + U + P + P + I + S$

Astrobits: Star Name Overlaps

1.	Alpha Virginis	Alpha Aurigae
2.	Alpha Coronae Borealis	Alpha Carinae
3.	Alpha Arietis	Alpha Hydrae
4.	Alpha Eridani	Alpha Bootis
5.	Alpha Orionis	Gamma Bootis
6.	Beta Leporis	Beta Persei
7.	80 Ursae Majoris	Alpha Canum Venaticorum
8.	Epsilon Ursae Majoris	Alpha Draconis
9.	Eta Ursae Majoris	Lambda Scorpii
10.	Zeta Ursae Majoris	Beta Sagittarii
11.	Lambda Draconis	Alpha Leporis
12.	Beta Eridani	Gamma Cygni
13.	Beta Cassiopeiae	Alpha Columbae
14.	Gamma Andromedae	Theta Leonis
15.	Epsilon Canis Majoris	Beta Draconis
16.	Kappa Orionis	Gamma Ursae Majoris
17.	Alpha Corvi	Theta Pegasi
18.	Kappa Ursae Majoris	Gamma Aquilae
19.	Gamma Geminorum	Gamma Capricorni
20.	Eta Canis Minoris	Alpha Ophiuchi

Search Games: Familiar Stars

ALGOL	CASTOR	PROXIMA CENTAURI
ALTAIR	DENEB	RIGEL
ANTARES	MIRA	SIRIUS
BELLATRIX	PLEIONE	VEGA
BETELGEUSE	POLARIS	
CANOPUS	POLLUX	

Search Games: Satellites

ARIEL	HYPERION	PHOBOS
CALLISTO	IAPETUS	PHOEBE
DEIMOS	IO	POSEIDON
DEMETER	JANUS	RHEA
DIONE	MIMAS	TETHYS
ENCELADUS	MIRANDA	TITAN
EUROPA	MOON	TITANIA
GANYMEDE	NEREID	TRITON
HERA	OBERON	UMBRIEL
HESTIA	PAN	

Search Games: Observatories

BRADLEY	LEANDER McCORMICK	SACRAMENTO PEAK
CHABOT	MARIA MITCHELL	SHATTUCK
DEARBORN	MARYLAND POINT	STRAWBRIDGE
DUDLEY	McMILLIN	MEMORIAL
FEATHER RIDGE	MORRISON	SOMMERS BAUSCH
GOODSELL	MOUNT CUBA	VAN VLECK
KIRKWOOD	MUMMY MOUNTAIN	WASHBURN
LADD	PORTAGE LAKE	

Search Games: Lunar Features

ALPHONSUS	GASSENDI	PLINIUS
ALPINE VALLEY	GRIMALDI	REGIOMONTANUS
APENNINES	HIPPARCHUS	TYCHO
CAUCASUS	HUMBOLDT	VEGA
CLAVIUS	LOCKYER	ZENO
DELAMBRE	OLBERS	
ERATOSTHENES	PICO	

Search Games: Famous Telescopes

ARMAGH-DUNSINK-	HALE	MILLS
HARVARD	HENRY	NORTHUMBERLAND
BRUCE	HOOKER	REYNOLDS
BURRELL	ISAAC NEWTON	THAW
CROSSLEY	MAYALL	VICTORIA
DORPAT	MERZ	WILSON
DYER	METCALF	WYETH

Search Games: Molecules

ACETALDEHYDE
ACETONITRILE
AMMONIA
CARBON MONOXIDE
CYANOGEN
ETHYL ALCOHOL
ETHYNYL

FORMALDEHYDE
FORMAMIDE
FORMIC ACID
HEAVY WATER
HYDROGEN
HYDROGEN CYANIDE
HYDROGEN SULFIDE

METHYL ALCOHOL
METHANIMINE
SILICON SULFIDE
THIOFORMALDEHYDE
WATER

Search Games: 20th Century Astronomers

BAADE
BARNARD
CANNON
CURTIS

HALE
HUBBLE
KUIPER
LEAVITT

LOWELL
MENZEL
RUSSELL
SEYFERT

SHAPLEY
SLIPHER
STRUVE
TRUMPLER

Astrocrostics

While most of the acrostic definitions are single words, others consist of two or more. Here are those in the latter category, with the precise number of letters indicated for each word.

Astrocrostic I

E. __ __ __ __ __   __ __ __ __ __

I. __ __   __ __ __ __ __ __ __ __

L. __ __ __ __ __   __ __ __ __ __

Astrocrostic II

C. __ __ __   __ __ __ __ __

D. __ __ __ __ __ __   __ __ __ __   __

__ __ __ __

E. __ __ __   __ __ __ __ __ __

G. __ __ __   __ __ __ __

L. __ __ __ __   __ __ __ __ __

M. __ __ __ __ __ __ __

__ __ __ __ __ __ __

N. __ __   __ __ __   __ __ __ __

P. __ __ __ __ __   __ __ __ __ __

Q. __ __   __ __ __   __ __ __ __ __

S. __ __ __ __   __ __ __ __ __

T. __ __ __ __ __ __   __ __

U. __ __ __   __ __ __ __ __ __ __

V. __ __ __   __   __ __ __ __ __

W. __ __   __ __ __

Astrocrostic III

A. __ __ __ __   __ __

E. __ __ __   __ __ __   __ __ __ __ __

    __ __ __ __

F. __ __ __   __ __ __ __ __

G. __ __ __ __ __   __ __ __ __ __

H. __ __ __ __   __ __ __ __

K. __ __ __ __ __   __ __ __ __ __

Astrocrostic IV

C. __ __ __ __   __ __

E. __ __ __   __ __   __ __ __ __ __ __ __

G. __ __ __ __ __   __ __ __ __ __ __

K. __ __   __ __ __   __ __ __

L. __ __ __   __ __   __ __ __

    __ __ __ __

N. __   __   __ __ __ __ __

P. __ __ __   __ __ __ __ __

Q. __ __ __ __ __   __ __ __ __ __ __

T. __ __ __ __ __   __ __

    __ __ __ __ __ __

U. __ __ __ __ __   __ __   __ __ __

    __ __ __

Z. __ __ __   __ __ __ __

Astrocrostic V

A. __ __ __ __ __ __ __ __ __ __ __ __

    __ __ __ __ __ __

B. __ __ __ __   __ __ __ __ __

D. __   __ __ __ __

F. __ __ __   __ __ __ __ __

H. __ __ __ __   __ __ __ __ __

I. __ __ __   __ __ __ __   __ __

    __ __ __ __ __ __

K. __ __ __ __   __ __ __ __

T. __ __   __ __ __ __ __ __ __ __ __

— 93 —

Astrocrostic VI

A. ___ ___ ___ ___ ___ ___
___ ___ ___ ___ ___ ___ ___ ___

B. ___ ___ ___ ___ ___ ___ ___ ___
___ ___ ___ ___ ___ ___ ___ ___

C. ___ ___ ___ ___ ___ ___
D. ___ ___ ___ ___
E. ___ ___ ___ ___ ___ ___ ___ ___ ___ ___ ___
F. ___ ___ ___ ___ ___ ___ ___ ___ ___
G. ___ ___ ___ ___ ___ ___ ___ ___
___ ___ ___ ___ ___ ___ ___

H. ___ ___ ___ ___ ___ ___ ___ ___
J. ___ ___ ___ ___ ___ ___ ___
M. ___ ___ ___ ___
O. ___ ___ ___ ___ ___ ___ ___ ___
Q. ___ ___ ___ ___ ___ ___ ___ ___ ___
R. ___ ___ ___ ___ ___ ___ ___
T. ___ ___ ___ ___ ___ ___ ___ ___ ___
___ ___ ___ ___ ___

U. ___ ___ ___ ___ ___ ___
V. ___ ___ ___ ___ ___ ___ ___ ___
___ ___ ___ ___ ___ ___ ___ ___ ___ ___

Y. ___ ___ ___ ___ ___ ___ ___ ___ ___ ___ ___ ___ ___ ___
___ ___ ___ ___ ___ ___

Z. ___ ___ ___ ___ ___ ___ ___ ___ ___
___ ___ ___ ___ ___ ___

FF. ___ ___ ___ ___ ___ ___ ___ ___
___ ___ ___ ___ ___ ___ ___

Saturn (Saturday)
*Gypsy Planet and
Dream Book*

Astrocrostic VII

A. __ __ __ __ __ __   __ __ __ __ __ __

D. __ __ __ __   __ __ __ __ __ __ __ __

E. __ __ __ __   __ __

__ __ __ __ __ __ __ __

F. __   __ __ __ __ __ __   __ __

H. __ __ __   __ __ __ __ __   __ __

__ __ __ __ __ __ __ __   __ __ __ __

J. __ __   __ __ __

L. __   __ __ __ __ __ __ __

O. __ __ __ __   __ __

P. __ __   __ __ __ __   __ __ __ __

S. __ __ __ __ __ __

__ __ __ __ __

T. __ __ __ __   __ __ __ __ __ __

U. __ __ __ __ __ __ __ __ __ __

__ __ __ __

Y. __   __ __ __ __ __ __

AA. __   __ __ __ __ __   __ __ __ __ __

CC. __ __   __ __ __ __ __ __   __ __

__ __ __ __   __ __ __

EE. __ __ __ __ __ __ __ __

__ __ __ __ __ __ __ __ __ __

GG. __ __ __   __ __ __ __ __

II. __ __ __ __ __ __ __ __   __ __ __ __ __ __ __

JJ. __ __   __ __ __ __ __ __

KK. __ __ __ __   __ __ __ __

Inu (The Dog)
Japanese Zodiac
from *Family Crests*

Answers

Astrobits: Name That Tune About the Moon

A. *Allegheny*
B. *Indiana*
C. *Carolina*
D. *Wabash*
E. *It's Only a Paper*
F. *Fly Me to the*
G. *Marshmallow*

H. *The _____ Is Low*
I. *New*
J. *Shine on Harvest*
K. *Over Miami*
L. *Lazy*
M. *The _____ Got in My Eyes*
N. *Once in a Blue*

O. *Underneath the Harlem*
P. *How High the*
Q. *Old Devil*
R. *Blue*
S. *Silver*
T. *When the _____ Comes Over the Mountain*

Astrobits: Cryptograms

1. *NEPTUNE HAS ONLY TWO KNOWN SATELLITES.*
2. *SATURN IS NOT THE ONLY PLANET WITH RINGS.*
3. *MERCURY IS THE PLANET CLOSEST TO THE SUN.*
4. *VENUS IS FREQUENTLY CALLED THE EARTH'S SISTER PLANET.*
5. *THE MOST MASSIVE PLANET IN THE SOLAR SYSTEM IS JUPITER.*
6. *THE LARGEST VOLCANO KNOWN IS NIX OLYMPICA ON MARS.*
7. *THE MOST REMOTE PLANET PRESENTLY KNOWN IS PLUTO.*
8. *THE ROTATIONAL AXIS OF URANUS LIES ALMOST IN THE ECLIPTIC.*

Astrobits: Songs for a Cloudy Night

1. *APRIL SHOWERS*
2. *STORMY WEATHER*
3. *BABY THE RAIN MUST FALL*
4. *SINGIN IN THE RAIN*
5. *A FOGGY DAY*
6. *HOW LONG HAS THIS BEEN GOING ON?*
7. *IT'S BEEN A LONG LONG TIME*
8. *LET IT SNOW, LET IT SNOW, LET IT SNOW*
9. *MISTY*
10. *TILL THE CLOUDS ROLL BY*
11. *LOST IN A FOG*

12. *OUT OF NOWHERE*
13. *OLE BUTTERMILK SKY*
14. *RAIN ON THE ROOF*
15. *THE DAY THE RAINS CAME*

Astrobits: Wordles

CLUSTER

1. *CELT*
2. *CLUE*
3. *CREST*
4. *CRUEL*
5. *CRUST*
6. *CULT*
7. *CURL*
8. *CUTE*
9. *ERUCT*
10. *LEST*
11. *LETS*
12. *LURE*
13. *LUST*
14. *LUTE*
15. *LUSTER*
16. *RECTUS*
17. *RELUCT*
18. *REST*
19. *RESULT*
20. *RULE*
21. *RUSE*
22. *RUST*
23. *SECT*
24. *SLUE*
25. *SLUR*
26. *SLUT*
27. *SUTLER*
28. *TRUE*
29. *TRUCE*
30. *ULCER*
31. *ULSTER*

PLANETS

1. *ANTE*
2. *APSE*
3. *ASPEN*
4. *EAST*
5. *ETNA*
6. *LANE*
7. *LAPSE*
8. *LAST*
9. *LATE*
10. *LEAN*
11. *LEAP*
12. *LEAST*
13. *LENS*
14. *LENT*
15. *LEPT*
16. *LEST*
17. *NAPE*
18. *NEAP*
19. *NEAT*
20. *NEST*
21. *PALE*
22. *PANE*
23. *PANEL*
24. *PANT*
25. *PAST*
26. *PASTE*
27. *PASTEL*
28. *PATE*
29. *PATEN*
30. *PEAL*
31. *PEAN*
32. *PEAT*
33. *PELT*
34. *PENAL*
35. *PENT*
36. *PEST*
37. *PLAN*
38. *PLANE*
39. *PLANT*
40. *PLAT*
41. *PLATE*
42. *PLEA*
43. *PLEAT*
44. *SALE*
45. *SALT*
46. *SATE*
47. *SEAL*
48. *SEAT*
49. *SENT*
50. *SEPAL*
51. *SEPT*
52. *SLANT*
53. *SLAP*
54. *SLAT*
55. *SLATE*
56. *SNAP*
57. *SPAE*
58. *SPAN*
59. *SPAT*
60. *SPEAN*
61. *SPENT*
62. *STALE*
63. *STAPLE*
64. *STEAL*
65. *STEP*
66. *TALE*
67. *TAPE*
68. *TAPS*
69. *TEAL*

Astrobits: Wordies

DENEBOLA

1. *ABED*	19. *BLEED*	37. *LADEN*
2. *ABLE*	20. *BLEND*	38. *LAND*
3. *ABODE*	21. *BLENDE*	39. *LANE*
4. *ADOBE*	22. *BLONDE*	40. *LEAD*
5. *AEON*	23. *BODE*	41. *LEADEN*
6. *ALONE*	24. *BOLA*	42. *LEAN*
7. *ANODE*	25. *BOLD*	43. *LEND*
8. *BADE*	26. *BOLE*	44. *LOAD*
9. *BALD*	27. *BOND*	45. *LOAN*
10. *BALE*	28. *BONE*	46. *LOBE*
11. *BAND*	29. *DALE*	47. *LODE*
12. *BANE*	30. *DEAL*	48. *LONE*
13. *BEAD*	31. *DEAN*	49. *NAPE*
14. *BEAN*	32. *DOLE*	50. *NEED*
15. *BEEN*	33. *EBON*	51. *NOBLE*
16. *BLADE*	34. *ELAN*	52. *NOEL*
17. *BLAND*	35. *ELAND*	53. *OLDEN*
18. *BLED*	36. *ENABLE*	

Astrobits: Dividing the Universe

A.	*0 = B*	*2 = U*	*4 = S*	*6 = F*	*8 = E*
	1 = N	*3 = A*	*5 = L*	*7 = P*	*9 = T*
B.	*0 = M*	*2 = N*	*4 = R*	*6 = S*	*8 = U*
	1 = Q	*3 = I*	*5 = V*	*7 = E*	*9 = A*
C.	*0 = P*	*2 = A*	*4 = G*	*6 = I*	*8 = F*
	1 = S	*3 = M*	*5 = R*	*7 = L*	
D.	*0 = L*	*2 = T*	*4 = S*	*6 = I*	*8 = N*
	1 = E	*3 = O*	*5 = A*	*7 = M*	*9 = P*
E.	*0 = N*	*2 = M*	*4 = G*	*6 = X*	*8 = I*
	1 = L	*3 = A*	*5 = E*	*7 = F*	*9 = Y*
F.	*0 = V*	*2 = N*	*4 = U*	*6 = R*	*8 = E*
	1 = O	*3 = P*	*5 = A*	*7 = S*	*9 = L*

Astrobits: Variable Stars

1. *d*	4. *e*	7. *l*	10. *k*	13. *c*
2. *h*	5. *j*	8. *m*	11. *n*	14. *b*
3. *f*	6. *i*	9. *g*	12. *a*	

Astrobits: Observatories

1. *c*	5. *t*	9. *b*	13. *n*	17. *s*	21. *m*
2. *g*	6. *h*	10. *v*	14. *p*	18. *l*	22. *k*
3. *j*	7. *o*	11. *e*	15. *r*	19. *u*	23. *f*
4. *d*	8. *i*	12. *q*	16. *a*	20. *x*	24. *w*

Astrobits: Constellation Names

1. d	5. i	9. q	13. c	17. n	21. m
2. h	6. r	10. p	14. k	18. e	22. f
3. t	7. b	11. a	15. g	19. v	
4. s	8. u	12. j	16. o	20. l	

Astrobits: Intelligence (?) Test

1. *Night — Our sun is closer than the other stars.*
2. *ASTRONOMERS*
3. *White — The hunter's campsite must have been at the north pole.*
4. *a. Following, because Jupiter had not yet reached opposition. b. East to west*
5. *Midnight*
6. *STAR: a. sat b. rat c. tar d. art e. as f. at*
7. *Mountain in South Africa from which early observations of the solar constant were made.*
8. *The examiners answer: A gnomon is a stick in the ground used for latitude determinations.*
   My answer: The remainder of a parallelogram after removing from one corner a similar parallelogram.
   Their answer: This examination must be taken seriously.
9. *Its son never sets.*
10. *No, the difference is about ¼ of a day's motion of the sun and is compensated by a leap year. Since 1900 was not a leap year, from 1897 to 1903 the accumulated effect was about 1¾ days. This difference will occur again in 2100.*
11. *In about 1,150 years.*
12. *a. the Taylor girls   b. Lewis Carroll*
13. *Tycho's dwarf*
14. *Supposedly got loose in a castle, wandered up stairs, drank too much beer, fell down stairs breaking a leg, and expired.*
15.

Eclipse year	—	*346.6200 days*
Tropical year	—	*365.2422 days*
Gregorian year	—	*365.2425 days*
Julian year	—	*365.2500 days*
Sidereal year	—	*365.2564 days*
Anomalistic year	—	*365.2596 days*

16. *Fly fishing*
17. *F. K. Edmondson of Indiana University, born in Milwaukee.*
18. *The parallax of Sirius is 0".375, thus the star's distance is 2.67 parsecs or 8.24×10^{18} cm. One angstrom is 10^{-8} cm. Thus, Sirius is 8.24×10^{26} angstroms away. Since a million million million giga angstroms is $10^6 \times 10^6 \times 10^6 \times 10^9 = 10^{27}$, the statement is false.*
19. *According to I.A.U. Commission 27 Information Bulletin on Variable Stars No. 1414, the last variable designated in Sagittarius was V 4026, thus there are that many variables in the constellation. The number of naked eye stars visible at one time is estimated to be somewhat less than 3,000.*
20. *Large Magellanic Cloud*

21. *Georgium Sidus (after George III)*
    J. Bode

22. *Carl Sagan*

23. *The total mass of the satellites is estimated to be 7.35 x 10^{26} grams; that of the asteroids 1.7 x 10^{24} grams. The statement is true.*

24. *Since fifth magnitude stars are 1/100 as bright as zero magnitude stars, 100 times more would be required; that is, 23,000.*

25. *Hydra with 1,303 square degrees; then come Virgo, 1,294; Ursa Major, 1,280; Cetus, 1,231; Hercules, 1,225.*

26. *None, the ladder rose with the boat.*

27. **A** *tied a string to the barometer, lowered the instrument to the ground from the top of the tower, and measured the length of the string.*
    B *kept the string tied to the barometer and set it swinging like a pendulum; from the pendulum's frequency she calculated the length of the string.*
    C *measured the length of the barometer; then, as he climbed down scaffolding used by painters, he counted the number of barometer lengths.*
    D *found the ratio of the barometer's height in a vertical position to the length of its shadow, then applied this ratio to the length of the tower's shadow.*
    E *dropped the barometer from the top of the tower; by measuring the time of fall, she was able to calculate the height.*
    F *presented the barometer as a gift to the observatory superintendent in exchange for the desired information.*
    (With apologies to Martin Gardner)

28. *He observed at different seasons, in warmer and warmer weather.*

29. *He dealt from the bottom, first to himself, then counterclockwise to the others.*

30. *Hadley's Quadrant and Goose*

31. *Winter*

32. *No, the sun is below the horizon. Yes, the moon appears monthly.*

33. **a.** *Auto dealer or grocery store;* **b.** *Grocer;* **c.** *Candy store;* **d.** *Television dealer;* **e.** *Candy store;* **f.** *Bookstore or auto dealer;* **g.** *Auto dealer or Astronomical Society of the Pacific;* **h.** *Defense Department;* **i.** *Auto dealer;* **j.** *NASA.*

34. *Sagittarius*

35. *Hydra*

Net (The Rat)
Japanese Zodiac
from *Family Crests*

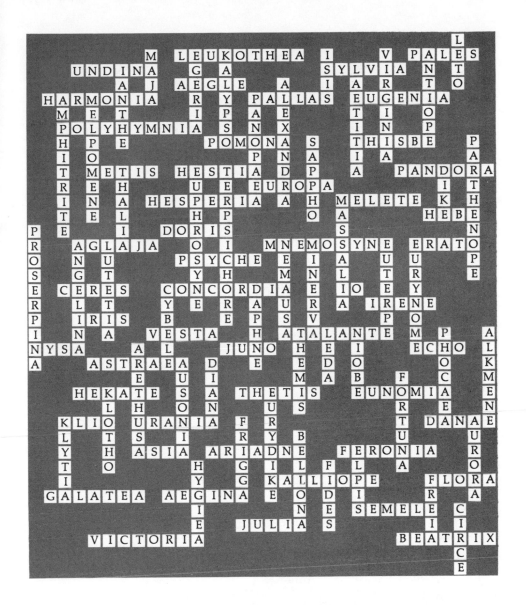

Astrobits: Who Observes Which Planet?

Mr. Mercury	Jupiter	Mr. Saturn	Mercury
Ms. Venus	Uranus	Mr. Uranus	Pluto
Mr. Mars	Venus	Mr. Neptune	Saturn
Mr. Jupiter	Neptune	Mr. Pluto	Mars

Astrobits: Physical Exercise

1. a. *The laws of physics hold true in all inertial reference frames. Thus, from the vantage point of one light bulb, the other is in motion; hence, the swinging one should break as frequently as the stationary one.*
   b. *Except when both bulbs broke, there was no deviation from the above.*
2. a. *The grass grew up and inwards.*
   b. *Up against the force of gravity, inwards against the centrifugal force outward.*

Astrobits: The Absent-minded Astronomers

Professor Apple

Astrobits: Telescope Allocations

	1st Dome	2nd Dome	3rd Dome	4th Dome	5th Dome
Telescope	150	50	16	84	36
State	Mass	Hoosier	Louisiana	Kansas	Texas
Tobacco	pipe	chews	cigarette	cigar	snuff
Drink	—	Coca-Cola	brandy	Coors	coffee
Wildlife	tarantula	scorpions	field mice	lady bugs	—

Astrobits: Signs and Symbols

1. J
2. D
3. I
4. N
5. W
6. K
7. R
8. Q
9. V
10. G
11. H
12. P
13. S
14. U
15. A
16. B
17. C
18. E
19. L
20. O
21. M
22. F
23. T

Atomic Composition of Constellations

1. BO O TES
2. CR AT ER
3. LU PU S
4. TA U RU S
5. LA C ER TA
6. C AR I NA
7. CARBON + IRIDIUM + CARBON + IODINE + NITROGEN + URANIUM + SULPHER
8. LITHIUM + BORON + RADIUM
9. MOLYBDENUM + NITROGEN + OXYGEN + CARBON + ERBIUM + OSMIUM
10. OXYGEN + CARBON + TANTALUM + NITROGEN + SULPHUR
11. PHOSPHORUS + IODINE + SULPHUR + CERIUM + SULPHUR
12. PHOSPHORUS + URANIUM + PHOSPHORUS + PHOSPHORUS + IODINE + SULPHUR

Astrobits: Messier Catalogue

M1	e	M20	g	M44	l	M64	f
M8	k	M27	b	M45	i	M97	j
M13	h	M31	d	M51	a	M104	c
M17	n	M42	o	M57	m		

Astrobits: Constellation Overlaps

1. CANCERIDANUS
2. PAVOLANS
3. CANES VENATICIRCINUS
4. AQUILACERTA
5. SAGITTAURUS
6. DRACORVUS
7. TRIANGULUM AUSTRALEO
8. MUSCARINA
9. LEO MINORION
10. MENSAGITTARIUS

Astrobits: Star Name Overlaps

1. SPICAPELLA
2. ALPHECCANOPUS
3. HAMALPHARD
4. ACHERNARCTURUS
5. BETELGEUSEGINUS
6. NIHALGOL
7. ALCOR CAROLI
8. ALIOTHUBAN
9. BENATNASHAULA
10. MIZARKAB
11. GIANSARNEB
12. CURSADR
13. CAPHAKT
14. ALMACHORT
15. ADARASTABAN
16. SAIPHECDA
17. ALCHIBAHAM
18. TALITARAZED
19. ALHENASHIRA
20. ALUDRASALHAGUE

What They Are Remembered For

1. f   Alfvén waves: waves that move perpendicularly through a magnetic field.
2. q   Avogadro number: the number of molecules in a mole.
3. k   Balmer series: lines of hydrogen in the visible spectrum.
4. v   Barnard's star: star with largest known proper motion.
5. z   Bok globule: spherical, compact, dark nebula.
6. M   Cassini's division: widest gap between the rings of Saturn.
7. F   Chandrasekhar limit: limiting mass for white dwarfs.
8. o   Compton effect: decrease in frequency of high-energy radiation caused by collision of a photon and free electron.
9. r   Coulomb collision: collision between two charged particles.
10. L   Doppler shift: displacement of spectral lines due to relative motion in the line of sight.
11. u   Ekman layer: layer within which the amplitude of a wave changes exponentially.
12. N   Faraday rotation: rotation of the plane of polarization of linearly polarized light.
13. J   Fermi gas: gas of electrons or fermions.
14. I   Gould's belt: band inclined to galactic plane with greatest concentration of naked-eye stars of spectral classes O and B.
15. D   Golay cell: gas bulb for detecting infrared radiation.
16. i   Halley's comet: famous, long-period comet.
17. a   Hubble constant: constant of propotionality in velocity-distance relation.

18. w   Johnson noise: Low-frequency electromagnetic radiation emitted by all bodies hotter than 0° Kelvin.
19. K   Kelvin contraction: contraction of a star due to radiation of thermal energy.
20. G   Kepler's laws: govern planetary motion.
21. l   Kerr black hole: rotating black hole.
22. d   Kirkwood gaps: regions where no asteroids occur.
23. A   Lemaitre universe: big-bang model of universe in which rate of expansion steadily decreases.
24. t   Lallemand camera: type of image tube.
25. p   Lowell Observatory: observatory in Flagstaff, Arizona.
26. H   Maksutov telescope: reflecting telescope with concave lens and spheroidal mirror.
27. E   Mie scattering: scattering of light by large particles.
28. b   Nicol prism: for detection of plane-polarized light.
29. c   Ockham's razor: any hypothesis should be free of all unnecessary assumptions.
30. n   Olbers' paradox: why is the sky dark at night?
31. C   Oort clouds: regions postulated to be the birthplace of comets.
32. y   Rankine scale: temperature scale that starts at 0° absolute with Fahrenheit divisions.
33. s   Roche lobe: first equipotential surface for two massive bodies that forms a figure eight enclosing them.
34. g   Schwarzschild radius: critical radius at which a massive body becomes a black hole.
35. e   Seyfert galaxy: galaxy with very high luminosity and very blue continuum radiation.
36. x   Stokes parameters: four parameters that must be evaluated to describe fully a beam of polarized light.
37. m   Stromgren sphere: more or less spherical region of ionized hydrogen surrounding a hot star.
38. h   Swan bands: spectral bands of carbon characteristic of carbon stars.
39. B   Taylor instability: hydrodynamic instability that occurs when there is a density inversion.
40. j   Wolf diagram: a plot used in star counting — the logarithm of the number of stars at successive magnitude limits versus the apparent magnitude.

Astrobits: Sun Words

A. *A SUN CION*	H. *SUN DAES*	O. *SUN FLOWER*
B. *SUN BATHE*	I. *SUN DIAL*	P. *SUN FISH*
C. *SUN BURN*	J. *SUN NA*	Q. *SUN DA*
D. *SUN KEN*	K. *SUN NY SIDE UP*	R. *SUN NY*
E. *SUN STONE*	L. *SUN DRIES*	S. *BO SUN*
F. *DAT SUN*	M. *SUN N*	T. *SUN DER*
G. *SUN DOWNERS*	N. *SUN DEW*	U. *SUN SPOT*

An Evening with William Shakespeare

1. D	9. B	17. G	25. M
2. L	10. K	18. A	26. E
3. B	11. H	19. C	27. B
4. O	12. H	20. F	28. N
5. N	13. B	21. F	29. E
6. H	14. J	22. C	
7. A	15. L	23. B	
8. I	16. I	24. K	

Search Games: Familiar Stars

A.	ALTAIR	G.	CASTOR	M.	ALGOL
B.	SIRIUS	H.	POLLUX	N.	ANTARES
C.	CANOPUS	I.	VEGA	O.	PLEIONE
D.	PROXIMA CENTAURI	J.	BETELGEUSE	P.	POLARIS
E.	MIRA	K.	RIGEL		
F.	DENEB	L.	BELLATRIX		

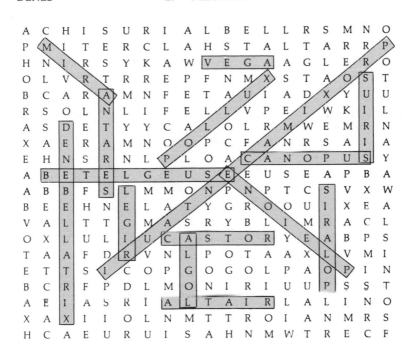

Search Games: Satellites

ARIEL	Uranus	HYPERION	Saturn	PHOBOS	Mars
CALLISTO	Jupiter	IAPETUS	Saturn	PHOEBE	Saturn
DEIMOS	Mars	IO	Jupiter	POSEIDON	Jupiter
DEMETER	Jupiter	JANUS	Saturn	RHEA	Saturn
DIONE	Saturn	MIMAS	Saturn	TETHYS	Saturn
ENCELADUS	Saturn	MIRANDA	Uranus	TITAN	Saturn
EUROPA	Jupiter	MOON	Earth	TITANIA	Uranus
GANYMEDE	Jupiter	NEREID	Neptune	TRITON	Neptune
HERA	Jupiter	OBERON	Uranus	UMBRIEL	Uranus
HESTIA	Jupiter	PAN	Jupiter		

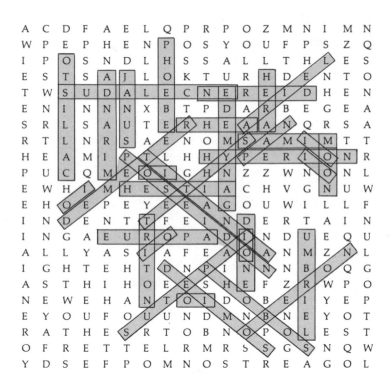

Tora (The Tiger)
Japanese Zodiac
from *Family Crests*

Search Games: Observatories

A. *DUDLEY: Albany, New York*
B. *KIRKWOOD: Bloomington, Illinois*
C. *SOMMERS BAUSCH: Boulder, Colorado*
D. *FEATHER RIDGE: Cedar Rapids, Iowa*
E. *LEANDER McCORMICK: Charlottesville, Virginia*
F. *McMILLIN: Columbus, Ohio*
G. *BRADLEY: Decatur, Georgia*
H. *DEARBORN: Evanston, Illinois*
I. *MORRISON: Fayette, Missouri*
J. *SHATTUCK: Hanover, New Hampshire*
K. *STRAWBRIDGE MEMORIAL: Haverford, Pennsylvania*
L. *WASHBURN: Madison, Wisconsin*
M. *VAN VLECK: Middletown, Connecticut*
N. *MARYLAND POINT: Riverside, Maryland*
O. *MARIA MITCHELL: Nantucket, Massachusetts*
P. *GOODSELL: Northfield, Minnesota*
Q. *CHABOT: Oakland, California*
R. *PORTAGE LAKE: Portage Lake, Michigan*
S. *LADD: Providence, Rhode Island*
T. *MUMMY MOUNTAIN: Scottsdale, Arizona*
U. *SACRAMENTO PEAK: Sunspot, New Mexico*
V. *MOUNT CUBA: Wilmington, Delaware*

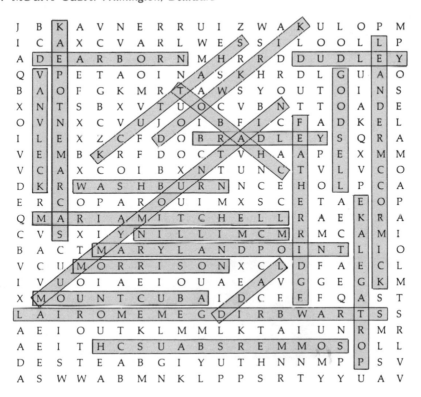

Search Games: Lunar Features

A. *APENNINES*
B. *CAUCASUS*
C. *CLAVIUS*
D. *GRIMALDI*
E. *HIPPARCHUS*
F. *PICO*
G. *ALPHONSUS*
H. *DELAMBRE*
I. *GASSENDI*

J. *HUMBOLDT*
K. *LOCKYER*
L. *OLBERS*
M. *PLINIUS*
N. *REGIOMONTANUS*
O. *TYCHO*
P. *VEGA*
Q. *ZENO*
R. *ALPINE VALLEY*
S. *ERATOSTHENES*

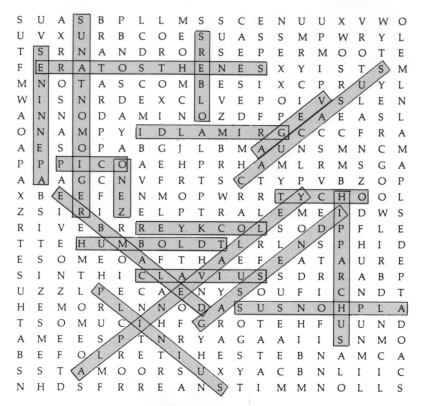

```
S  U  A  S  B  P  L  L  M  S  S  C  E  N  U  U  X  V  W  O
U  V  X  U  R  B  C  O  E  S  U  A  S  S  M  P  W  R  Y  L
T  S  R  N  A  N  D  R  O  R  S  E  P  E  R  M  O  O  T  E
F  E  R  A  T  O  S  T  H  E  N  E  S  X  Y  I  S  T  S  M
M  N  O  T  A  S  C  O  M  B  E  S  I  X  C  P  R  U  Y  L
W  I  S  N  R  D  E  X  C  L  V  E  P  O  I  V  S  L  E  N
A  N  N  O  D  A  M  I  N  O  Z  D  F  P  E  A  E  A  S  L
O  N  A  M  P  Y  I  D  L  A  M  I  R  G  C  C  C  F  R  A
A  E  S  O  P  A  B  G  J  L  B  M  A  U  N  S  M  N  C  M
P  P  P  I  C  O  A  E  H  P  R  H  A  M  L  R  M  S  G  A
A  A  A  G  C  N  V  F  R  T  S  C  T  Y  P  V  B  Z  O  P
X  B  E  E  F  N  E  N  M  O  P  W  R  R  T  Y  C  H  O  L
Z  S  I  R  I  Z  E  L  P  T  R  A  L  E  M  E  I  D  W  S
R  I  V  E  B  R  R  E  Y  K  C  O  L  S  O  D  P  F  L  E
T  T  E  H  U  M  B  O  L  D  T  L  R  L  N  S  P  H  I  D
E  S  O  M  E  O  A  F  T  H  A  E  F  E  A  T  A  U  R  E
S  I  N  T  H  I  C  L  A  V  I  U  S  S  D  R  R  A  B  P
U  Z  Z  L  P  E  C  A  E  N  Y  S  O  U  F  I  C  N  D  T
H  E  M  O  R  L  N  N  O  D  A  S  U  S  N  O  H  P  L  A
T  S  O  M  U  C  I  H  F  G  R  O  T  E  H  F  U  U  N  D
A  M  E  E  S  P  T  N  R  Y  A  G  A  A  I  I  S  N  M  O
B  E  F  O  L  R  E  T  I  H  E  S  T  E  B  N  A  M  C  A
S  S  T  A  M  O  O  R  S  U  X  Y  A  C  B  N  L  I  I  C
N  H  D  S  F  R  R  E  A  N  S  T  I  M  M  N  O  L  L  S
```

U (The Hare)
Japanese Zodiac
from *Family Crests*

Search Games: Famous Telescopes

A. *WYETH*
B. *THAW*
C. *ARMAGH-DUNSINK-HARVARD*
D. *NORTHUMBERLAND*
E. *MILLS*
F. *REYNOLDS*
G. *VICTORIA*
H. *MERZ*
I. *MAYALL*
J. *CROSSLEY*

K. *WILSON*
L. *METCALF*
M. *HOOKER*
N. *HALE*
O. *HENRY*
P. *DORPAT*
Q. *ISAAC NEWTON*
R. *DYER*
S. *BURRELL*
T. *BRUCE*

Search Games: Molecules

A. *HYDROGEN*
B. *WATER*
C. *HYDROGEN SULFIDE*
D. *CYANOGEN*
E. *CARBON MONOXIDE*
F. *HYDROGEN CYANIDE*
G. *SILICON SULFIDE*
H. *HEAVY WATER*
I. *AMMONIA*
J. *FORMALDEHYDE*

K. *ETHYNYL*
L. *METHYL ALCOHOL*
M. *ACETONITRILE*
N. *ACETALDEHYDE*
O. *METHANIMINE*
P. *THIOFORMALDEHYDE*
Q. *ETHYL ALCOHOL*
R. *FORMIC ACID*
S. *FORMAMIDE*

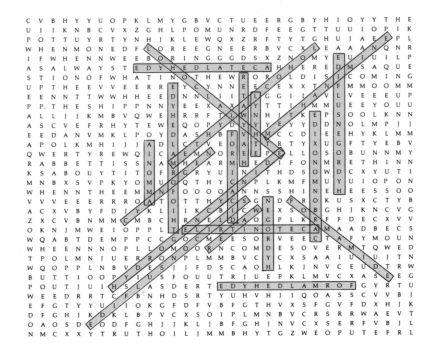

Saru (The Monkey)
Japanese Zodiac
from *Family Crests*

Search Games: 20th Century Astronomers

1. *Russell*	G.	5. *Hubble*	H.	9. *Struve*	K.	13. *Barnard*	C.
2. *Baade*	E.	6. *Menzel*	I.	10. *Seyfert*	M.	14. *Hale*	D.
3. *Shapley*	O.	7. *Kuiper*	J.	11. *Curtis*	P.	15. *Trumpler*	A.
4. *Slipher*	F.	8. *Lowell*	L.	12. *Cannon*	B.	16. *Leavitt*	N.

```
G V T H S Q T R A E Y F G I P K W L M O
B A C S D T U R N K L F C K Q P O A S L
L G O O D F E L E L O P T U T U I M N X
W H A A O L M H J F E W R I P L L V C S
P O L X C R V B T Y Y E L P A H S S H A
W H E I C E F I R G G E C E W U B J K F
C V W K G L U I Y L V B S R S B D V A K
T H E R R P A O L L E O P T A B A A D E
L C V R T M E N Z E L L E W O L S X I P
F D O X C U G U E S A E E U F E D P I L
A U U R T R O D E S H V E R U I C L M N
K E R F T T T U I U S I T R U C U R C
O C V S T Y I X C R U S T T B A A D D F
L E N Z F M L Z T E Q U Y V T I N J K P
B R E H P I L S L I O F E R Q U N X C V
P H E R L I S F G M C E R Y F B O L L O
D A R N A R B B A X X A B B A R N A R D
B A R Y A C E V G T H D N M Y O P R E E
```

Astrocrostic I

Author: none Title: none

*THE COSMOLOGICAL PRINCIPLE STATES THAT THE UNIVERSE LOOKS VERY
MUCH THE SAME FROM ANY LOCATION AND IN ALL DIRECTIONS*

A. *HIDALGO*	F. *INCLINATION*	K. *TETHYS*
B. *MODEST*	G. *LOVELL*	L. *PRIME FOCUS*
C. *KAPTEYN*	H. *SCHOTT*	M. *EROS*
D. *VERNAL*	I. *AE HERCULIS*	N. *COMA*
E. *CANIS MINOR*	J. *THETA*	

Astrocrostic II

Author: none Title: Astronomers Drinking Song (sing to "Yankee Doodle")

COLD WATER MAKES NO LUCKY HITS
ON MYSTERIES THE HEAD RUNS;
SMALL DRINK LET KEPLER TIME HIS WITS
ON THE REGULAR POLYHEDRONS;
HE TOOK TO WINE AND IT CHANGED THE CHIME,
HIS GENIUS SWEPT AWAY, SIR,
THROUGH AREA VARYING AS THE TIME
AT THE RATE OF A BOTTLE A DAY SIR!

A. *ARISTARCHOS*
B. *SLOUGH*
C. *THE FIRST*
D. *RESIST WAIT A MITE*
E. *OWL NEBULA*
F. *NETWORK*
G. *OPEN SEA*
H. *METHANE*

I. *ETHER*
J. *RITTER*
K. *SHELL*
L. *DELAY TIMES*
M. *RITCHEY CHRETIEN*
N. *IN THE WEST*
O. *NOVALIKE*
P. *KIRKWOODS GAPS*

Q. *IN THE HYADES*
R. *NUCLIDES*
S. *GAMMA HYDRI*
T. *SHAPLEY A*
U. *ORTHO HYDROGEN*
V. *NOT A DATUM*
W. *GK TAU*

Astrocrostic III

Author: Edwin Robinson From: O(ctaves)

AND THUS WE DIE,
STILL SEARCHING LIKE POOR OLD ASTRONOMERS
WHO TOTTER OFF TO BED AND GO TO SLEEP
TO DREAM OF UNTRIANGULATED STARS

A. *EAST OF*
B. *DARKEST*
C. *WIDMANSTATTEN*
D. *ISLE*
E. *NOT THE RIGHT STAR*

F. *RED DWARF*
G. *OUTER SPACE*
H. *BLUE EDGE*
I. *IMOTO*
J. *NULLS*

K. *SPRING, FLOOD*
L. *OORT*
M. *NODAL*
N. *OH, OO*

Hitsuji (The Goat)
Japanese Zodiac
from *Family Crests*

Astrocrostic IV

Author: Galileo Galilei Title: Star Messenger

THERE REMAINS THE MATTER WHICH SEEMS TO ME TO DESERVE TO BE
CONSIDERED THE MOST IMPORTANT IN THIS WORK NAMELY THAT I
SHOULD DISCLOSE AND PUBLISH TO THE WORLD THE OCCASION OF
DISCOVERING FOUR PLANETS NEVER SEEN FROM THE VERY BEGINNING OF
THE WORLD UP TO OUR OWN TIMES.

A.	GOTTINGEN	J.	LUTHER	S.	METHOD
B.	ALFONSINE	K.	IN THE RAM	T.	EPOCH OF MINIMUM
C.	LINE OF	L.	LOW IN THE WEST	U.	STORM ON THE SUN
D.	ISHTAR	M.	EVERSHED	V.	SOUTHERNMOST
E.	LAW OF PHYSICS	N.	I S BOWEN	W.	ENDOTHERMIC
F.	EVANSTON	O.	SPECTROSCOPE	X.	NEVER
G.	OUTER CORONA	P.	THE ORBIT	Y.	GRID
H.	GRAVITY	Q.	ADDED KLOTHO	Z.	EBB TIDE
I.	ALMS	R.	REDDEST	AA.	REVIEWS

Astrocrostic V

Author: Isaac Newton Title: Principia

THE GRAVITATIONAL FORCE BETWEEN ANY TWO PARTICLES IS PROPOR-
TIONAL TO THE PRODUCT OF THEIR MASSES AND INVERSELY PROPOR-
TIONAL TO THE SQUARE OF THE DISTANCE BETWEEN THEIR CENTERS OF
GRAVITY

A.	INTERSTELLAR MATTER	H.	WHITE DWARF	O.	NOVAE
B.	SOFT LANDER	I.	THE RIFT IN CYGNUS	P.	CHART
C.	ASTROLOGY	J.	OTTO	Q.	ICEY
D.	A PAIR	K.	NEON TUBE	R.	PORTER
E.	CASTOR	L.	PROBE	S.	ISOPHOTE
F.	NEW HAVEN	M.	REDSHIFT	T.	AQ TELESCOPII
G.	EVENT	N	ISOTOPE		

Tori (The Cock)
Japanese Zodiac
from Family Crests

Astrocrostic VI

Author: James H. Jeans Title: The Stars in Their Courses

IF WE HAD BEEN BORN ON VENUS OR JUPITER WE SHOULD HAVE LIVED OUR LIVES WITHOUT EVER SEEING THROUGH THE CLOUDS AND SO SHOULD HAVE KNOWN NOTHING OF THE BEAUTY AND POETRY OF THE NIGHT SKY AND NOTHING OF THE INTELLECTUAL EXCITEMENT AND JOY OF TRYING TO DECIPHER THE MEANING OF THE VAST PANORAMA OF LIGHTS WHICH ARE SCATTERED ROUND US IN ALL DIRECTIONS IN SPACE

A. *JULIAN CALENDAR*
B. *ABSOLUTE MAGNITUDE*
C. *MILKY WAY*
D. *EPH T*
E. *STANDING WAVE*
F. *HENRI LHOTE*
G. *JOHANNES KEPLER*
H. *EDDINGTON A S*
I. *ALBEDO*
J. *NOVA CYGNI*
K. *SLIPHER*
L. *TOUGH*
M. *HOT WHITE*
N. *ECHO*
O. *SUDDEN FOG*
P. *TODD*
Q. *ASHEN LIGHT*

R. *RT CORVI*
S. *SOUTHERN*
T. *IO UNDINA AND IANTHE*
U. *NORTH OF*
V. *THE THEORY OF RELATIVITY*
W. *HUTH*
X. *EUDOXUS*
Y. *INVERSE COMPTON EFFECT*
Z. *RESOLVING POWER*
AA. *CV*
BB. *O B*
CC. *U T*
DD. *RHEA*
EE. *SHEWN*
FF. *EINSTEIN EFFECT*
GG. *SOUTH*

Mi (The Serpent)
Japanese Zodiac
from *Family Crests*

Astrocrostic VII

Author: Walt Whitman Title: When I Heard the Learnd Astronomer

WHEN I HEARD THE LEARND ASTRONOMER
WHEN THE PROOFS THE FIGURES WERE RANGED IN COLUMNS BEFORE ME
WHEN I WAS SHOWN THE CHARTS AND DIAGRAMS TO ADD DIVIDE
    AND MEASURE THEM
WHEN I SITTING HEARD THE ASTRONOMER WHERE HE LECTURED
    WITH MUCH APPLAUSE IN THE LECTURE ROOM
HOW SOON UNACCOUNTABLE I BECAME TIRED AND SICK
TILL RISING AND GLIDING OUT I WANDERD OFF BY MYSELF
    IN THE MYSTICAL MOIST NIGHT AIR
AND FROM TIME TO TIME LOOKD UP IN PERFECT SILENCE AT THE STARS

A. WHITE DWARF
B. ANDROMEDA
C. LIGHTYEAR
D. THE ECLIPTIC
E. WEST OF FLAGSTAFF
F. H AND K NA
G. INFRARED
H. THE THIRD OR HARMONIC LAW
I. METHANE
J. AB MUS
K. NEPTUNE
L. W HERSCHEL
M. HDC
N. EARTHLIGHT
O. NAGY B
P. IT WAS IRIS
Q. HESIOD
R. EPHEMERIS
S. ANGULAR MOMENTUM
T. RADIO WINDOW

U. DESCENDING NODE
V. TITIUS
W. HESS
X. ECCENTRICITY
Y. L NUMBER
Z. EVECTION
AA. A WORLD MODEL
BB. RHEITA
CC. NO FLARE ON THE SUN
DD. DEIMOS
EE. ABSOLUTE MAGNITUDE
FF. SUMMER
GG. THE FIRST
HH. REDDENING
II. OPTICAL WINDOW
JJ. NO MARKET
KK. OTTO HAHN
LL. MESSIER
MM. ECOSPHERE
NN. RITTENHOUSE

I (The Boar)
Japanese Zodiac
from *Family Crests*